# Foundations for Algebra: Year 1

**Managing Editors:**

Elizabeth Coyner
    Bear River School
Beverly Brockhoff
    Glen Edwards Middle School

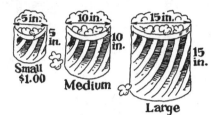

**Illustrator:**

Jonathan Weast
    Weast & Weast Illustration Studio
    Sacramento, California

**Technical Assistance:**

Bethany Sorbello
    CPM Educational Program
Thu Pham
    The CRESS Center
    University of California, Davis

*Developed by CPM Educational Program*

**Program Directors:**

Judith Kysh
    Departments of Mathematics and Education
    San Francisco State University
Tom Sallee
    Department of Mathematics
    University of California, Davis
Brian Hoey
    CPM Educational Program

v 3.0

# Credits for the First Edition

## Substantially Revised (2000, 2001)
### by

Heidi Ackley
Steve Ackley
Elizabeth Baker
Bev Brockhoff
Ellen Cafferata
Elizabeth Coyner
Sara Effenbeck
William Funkhouser
Brian Hoey
Carol Jancsi

Judy Kysh
Kris Petersen
Robert Petersen
Edwin Reed
Stacy Rocklein
Kristie Sallee
Tom Sallee
Howard Webb
Kaye Whitney
Jon Wickham

## Pilot Edition Contributing Editors (1999)

Heidi Ackley
Steve Ackley
Bev Brockhoff
Ellen Cafferata
Elizabeth Coyner
Scott Coyner
Kathleen Davies
Merci Del Rosario
Virginia Downing
Sara Effenbeck
Alice Elstien
William Ford

William Funkhouser
Bruce Grip
Stephen Inouye
Carol Jancsi
Alvin Mendle, Jr.
Pattie Montgomery
Edwin Reed
Gail Standiford
Gale Sunderland
Howard Webb
Kaye Whitney
Jon Wickham

## Technical Assistance

Jennifer Buddenhagen
Grace Chen
Ankit Jain
Janelle Petersen

Jeremy Tauzer
David Trombly
Erika Wallender
Emily Wheelis

# Foundations for Algebra: Year 1
## First Edition
# Table of Contents

# A Note to Parents, Students, and Teachers

Welcome to *Foundations for Algebra: Year 1.*

This textbook will prepare students for future Algebra courses. It was also written to consolidate the core ideas of previous mathematics courses, so that it will serve students of varied mathematics backgrounds. The contents of this course are many of the fundamental ideas and procedures necessary to be successful in subsequent mathematics courses and many careers. Classroom teachers wrote the lessons to present these ideas in ways that have proven successful with their students. The course also meets local, state, and national curriculum standards.

The investigations, problems, and practice exercises are designed to develop the students' logical and mathematical reasoning skills. The sequence of problems leads to understanding the reasoning behind the mathematical concepts. Students complete guided investigations that explore and develop ideas, then practice them along with procedural skills in subsequent chapters. Many problems use the mathematics in situations like those encountered by students and adults in their daily activities and business settings.

In order to be successful in mathematics it is critical that students actively participate in their learning. This means that each student must read and work all of the problems. Students need to discuss mathematical concepts and the reasoning involved in the steps of their solutions. In order to provide these discussion opportunities, students are encouraged to work with a study partner and in study teams both inside and outside the classroom. It is critical that students complete ALL of the assignments, including homework, to develop their individual skills. Equally important is that students take accurate, complete notes and ask questions about any problem, question, or concept that they find confusing or difficult to understand.

There are two additional resources that the authors designed to help students be successful in this course. The first is the mathematics Tool Kit that contains most of the ideas a student needs to know in the course. Tool Kit entries appear in the student text and in a Tool Kit booklet. The other is the *Foundations for Algebra Parent Guide*. The guide is sometimes available from the classroom teacher or the school library. It is available through the Internet at www.cpm.org. It may also be purchased directly from CPM Educational Program for $20 plus $3 shipping (California residents please add local sales tax to the $20) by sending a check to CPM, 1233 Noonan Drive, Sacramento, CA 95822.

# Millions and Billions

Chapter 6

# Chapter 6
*Millions and Billions:* **RATIO AND PROPORTION**

Learning to set up and solve proportions may be the most useful mathematical tool you develop beyond learning the basic operations of addition, subtraction, multiplication, and division. You use proportions to solve problems involving percents, discount rates, maps, scale models, and more.

In this chapter you will have the opportunity to:

- set up and solve proportions for problems and situations, including:
  - distance, rate, and time problems.
  - unit price and unit rate problems.
  - percent problems.
  - discount problems.
  - scale drawings and models including maps.
  - problems involving similar geometric figures.
  - currency exchange problems.

- change fractions to decimals using division.

- estimate percents.

- find least common multiples for pairs of integers.

- calculate probabilities of complementary events.

Read the problem below, but **do not try to solve it now**. What you learn over the next few days will enable you to solve it.

---

MB-0.　　How many pages of a newspaper would you need to have <u>one million</u> printed symbols? Just how big is "one million"? Our solar system contains nine planets that revolve around the sun at various distances from as close as 59 <u>million</u> kilometers to more than 5 <u>billion</u> kilometers. Not all the planets are the same size, either. How would you design a model that shows the relative distances between the planets? How would you build a model that shows the relative sizes of the planets? What would you have to know to make your model fit on one sheet of paper? to fit on your desk? to make good use of the land available on a football field?

---

Number Sense

Algebra and Functions

Mathematical Reasoning

Measurement and Geometry

Statistics, Data Analysis, & Probability

# Chapter 6
## Millions and Billions: RATIO AND PROPORTION

MB-1.  Determine the value of each variable in the equations below.

a)    $4n = 36$                              b)    $25 = 5m$

MB-2.    When you solved the equations in the last problem, did you use division to "undo" the multiplication problem?

For example, in part (a) above, if you divide 36 by 4, you undo the multiplication to see that n must be 9.

In general, all we have to do to solve equations is to "undo" them using the inverse operation at each step. List the inverse operation for each of the following arithmetic operations.

a)    addition          b)    subtraction          c)    multiplication          d)    division

MB-3.    For her homework Morgan had to list pairs of equal ratios. She wrote the correct proportion $\frac{2}{3} = \frac{6}{9}$. After completing several problems she noticed a pattern. When two fractions are equal you can multiply the numbers on the diagonals (shown at right with arrows) and get the same product. Write the multiplication problems from the proportion $\frac{5}{6} = \frac{10}{12}$ to show you know what Morgan means by multiply diagonally.

$2(9) = 6(3)$

$18 = 18$

MB-4.    Morgan showed her dad the pattern she discovered. He is an electrical engineer and wanted to show her why her pattern works. Mr. Petersen talked Morgan through these steps using the proportion $\frac{48}{57} = \frac{32}{38}$.

a)    First, Morgan had to multiply both sides of the equation by 57. She then had $\frac{32}{38}(57)$ on the right side of her equation. What did she have on the left?

b)    Since Morgan knew that the original equation was true, how did she know that the second equation was true?

c)    Next she multiplied both sides of the new equation from part (a) by 38. On the left side, she then had $(48)(38)$. What did she have on the right?

d)    The two multiplications which Morgan did are known as **cross multiplying.** Why do you think it has that name?

e)    Since Morgan started with two equal ratios, how did she know that she ended up with two equal numbers?

**MB-5.** Use cross multiplication to find the values of x that make the following proportions true.

a) $\dfrac{x}{20} = \dfrac{15}{60}$     b) $\dfrac{20}{x} = \dfrac{8}{10}$     c) $\dfrac{x}{35} = \dfrac{28}{49}$

**MB-6.** We have used the Identity Property of Multiplication, ratio tables, and diagrams to find equivalent fractions. Another way to find equivalent fractions is to write a proportion.

Ali types 60 words in two minutes. She estimates that her history report is 540 words long. She wants to know the number of minutes it will take her to type her whole report. Solving this problem will involve three steps.

Copy these steps into your notebook.

1.  The first step is setting up an equation. Notice that both rates compare minutes to words. We want to find the number that will make the fractions equal.

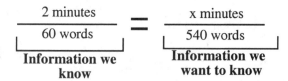

2.  Multiply the diagonals to write an equation without fractions.

$$\dfrac{2}{60} \bowtie \dfrac{x}{540}$$

$$(2) \cdot (540) = (60) \cdot (x) \text{ (without the units)}$$

3.  Solve the resulting equation.     $1080 = 60x \;\Rightarrow\; x = 18$

To solve a proportion:

- Copy the equation.
- Multiply the diagonals to write an equation without fractions.
- Solve the resulting equation.

Use the process outlined above to solve these proportions:

a) $\dfrac{x}{10} = \dfrac{6}{15}$     b) $\dfrac{12}{9} = \dfrac{8}{x}$     c) $\dfrac{8}{10} = \dfrac{x}{15}$

d) Use the Giant **1** to show that the fractions in part (c) are equivalent.

**MB-7.** Juan makes four out of nine shots that he takes in basketball. If he maintains this rate, how many shots will he make if he shoots 135 times? Use the process described in the previous problem to find the answer.

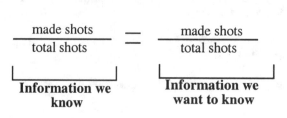

MB-8.

| SOLVING PROPORTIONS USING CROSS MULTIPLICATION |
|---|

When a proportion has one variable, multiplying the diagonals, known as **CROSS MULTIPLICATION**, results in an equation without fractions.

$$\frac{3 \text{ books}}{2 \text{ weeks}} = \frac{x \text{ books}}{18 \text{ weeks}}$$

$$\frac{3}{2} = \frac{x}{18}$$

Example: If Cindy can read 3 books in 2 weeks, how many books can she read in 18 weeks?

$$3(18) = 2x$$
$$54 = 2x$$
$$27 = x$$

Make these notes in your Tool Kit to the right of the double-lined box.

The broker will pay the farmer $5.00 for every 30 pounds of walnuts. Write and solve a proportion to find how much she will pay for 1500 pounds of walnuts.

MB-9.    Solve each of the following proportions.

a) $\frac{3 \text{ minutes}}{60 \text{ words}} = \frac{x \text{ minutes}}{360 \text{ words}}$

b) $\frac{2 \text{ days}}{15 \text{ hot dogs}} = \frac{x \text{ days}}{90 \text{ hot dogs}}$

c) $\frac{4 \text{ days}}{5 \text{ pizzas}} = \frac{x \text{ days}}{35 \text{ pizzas}}$

d) Choose one of the problems from parts (a) through (c) and write a word problem for it.

MB-10.

While our fraction-decimal-percent grids are helpful when we need to convert a fraction to decimal form, the grids are not always practical. The Giant **1** can be used to write an equivalent fraction with a denominator or 10, 100, or 1000 which can then be written in decimal form or percent form. For example $\frac{3}{8} \cdot \frac{125}{125} = \frac{375}{1000} = 0.375$ or 37.5%. Use the Giant **1** to find the decimal and percent forms for each fraction.

a) $\frac{5}{8}$

b) $\frac{4}{5}$

c) $\frac{11}{10}$

MB-11.

There is another way to convert a fraction into decimal from. Remember in the fraction $\frac{3}{2}$ the horizontal bar between the 3 and the 2 tells us to divide 3 by 2. At right $3 \div 2$ is written as a long division problem.

$$\begin{array}{r} 1.5 \\ 2\overline{)3.0} \\ -2\phantom{.0} \\ \hline 1\,0 \\ -1\,0 \\ \hline 0 \end{array}$$

You can convert any fraction to a decimal this way. Convert each of the following fractions to decimals.

a) $\frac{1}{4}$

b) $\frac{4}{5}$

c) $\frac{5}{4}$

d) $\frac{1}{8}$

**MB-12.** Draw a number line from 0 to 2 like the one below. Then write the following numbers in their correct places on the number line.

$$\frac{12}{11} \qquad 0.2 \qquad \frac{13}{26} \qquad 1.5 \qquad \frac{1}{8} \qquad 1.9 \qquad \frac{7}{8} \qquad 1.09 \qquad \frac{3}{5} \qquad 1.19$$

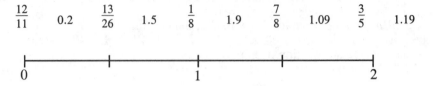

**MB-13.** In most of the following problems, a mistake was made. Find the mistake, and explain what it is, then finish each problem correctly. If the problem is correct, write "Correct."

a)

$$7 \cdot 8$$
$$56$$

b)  (24) + ((64 ÷ 8 − 8))

$$24 + (8 - 8)$$
$$24 + 0$$
$$24$$

c)  $24 - 16 \div 2 \cdot 8$

$$8 \div 2 \cdot 8$$
$$4 \cdot 8$$
$$32$$

d)  (2 ( 6 − 24)) + (2· 8)

$$2 \cdot (-18) + 16$$
$$2 \cdot (-2)$$
$$-4$$

**MB-14.** **Algebra Puzzles** Solve these equations. Write your answers as decimals or fractions.

a)  $2y + 3 = 4$

b)  $4x - 5 = -8$

**MB-15.** Recall that a factor of a number divides it evenly. For example, 4 and 6 are factors of 12.

a)  Find all the factors of 24.

b)  Find the smallest number that has 1, 2, 3, 4, and 5 as factors.

c)  Find the second smallest number that has 1, 2, 3, 4, and 5 as factors.

d)  Find the smallest number that has 1, 2, 3, 4, 5, 6, 7, 8, 9, and 10 as factors.

MB-16. Now that we have started a new chapter, it is time for you to organize your binder.

    a)    Put the work from the last chapter in order and keep it in a separate folder.

    b)    When this is completed, write "I have organized my binder."

MB-17. Follow your teacher's directions for practicing mental math.

MB-18.  Alfredo recently returned from a trip to Mexico with his parents. He brought back 75 pesos. The exchange rate was 9.454 pesos per dollar. What is the value of Alfredo's pesos in U.S. dollars? Solve the proportion above right. Be sure to show and label all your work.

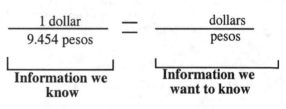

$$\frac{1 \text{ dollar}}{9.454 \text{ pesos}} = \frac{\text{dollars}}{\text{pesos}}$$

**Information we know**      **Information we want to know**

MB-19. Use the exchange rates provided by your teacher to convert each of the following quantities into U.S. dollars.

    a)    15 Australian Dollars         b)    25 Brazilian Reales

    c)    82 Canadian Dollars.

MB-20.    Jack and Amber were looking at a map of Yosemite Valley, which is located in Yosemite
National Park in California.  Here is the scale: 2 inches on the map represents 3 miles in
the park.  Jack and Amber want to hike from Yosemite Lodge to Curry Village.

a)    The length of the hike on the map is $5\frac{1}{2}$ inches.  Write and solve a proportion to
find the length of the hike in miles.

b)    Jack and Amber know that they can hike 5 miles every 2 hours.  They want to know
how long it will take to hike from Yosemite Lodge to Curry Village.  Use your result
in part (a) to write and solve a proportion to find how long the hike will take them.


MB-21.    Complete the ratio table, then answer the questions below.

| 5 | 10 | 15 | | 25 | | 35 | |
|---|----|----|----|----|----|----|----|
| 7 | | | 28 | | 42 | | 56 |

a)    Look at the top row and then at the bottom row.  What is the smallest number that
appears in <u>both</u> rows?

b)    If you extend the ratio table, what is the next number that both rows have in common?

c)    The top row is a list of multiples of 5.  The bottom row is a list of multiples of 7.
Your answers to parts (a) and (b) are called **common multiples** of 5 and 7.  Write a
sentence explaining why this name makes sense.

d)    Your answer to part (a) is also called the **least common multiple** of 5 and 7.  Write
a sentence explaining why this name makes sense.

## LEAST COMMON MULTIPLES

The **LEAST COMMON MULTIPLE** of two or more integers is the smallest positive integer that is divisible by <u>both</u> (or all) of the integers.

Example:      Use a ratio table to find the least common multiple of 3 and 5.

| 3 | 6 | 9 | 12 | ⑮ |
|---|---|---|----|----|
| 5 | 10 | ⑮ | 20 | 25 |

15 is the least common multiple because it is the smallest positive integer divisible by both 3 and 5.

Make these notes in your Tool Kit to the right of the double-lined box.

In your own words describe how to find the least common multiple of two integers.

---

MB-23.

Sometimes when we use long division to convert a fraction into a decimal form one or more digits repeat. We indicate that a decimal form has repeating digits by writing a bar over any digit which repeats.

$$\begin{array}{r} 0.22\ldots = 0.\overline{2} \\ 9\overline{)2.0} \\ -1\ 8 \\ \hline 2\ 0 \\ -1\ 8 \\ \hline 2 \end{array}$$

Use long division to convert each fraction to a decimal. Use bar notation for repeating decimals.

a)   $\dfrac{1}{3}$        b)   $\dfrac{11}{30}$        c)   $\dfrac{7}{8}$        d)   $\dfrac{4}{9}$

---

MB-24.

You can also convert a mixed number to a fraction using long division and addition. For example, if you wish to convert $4\frac{3}{5}$ to a decimal, use long division to convert $\frac{3}{5}$ to 0.6, and then add 4 to get 4.6. Convert each of the following fractions to decimals.

a)   $4\dfrac{3}{4}$        b)   $5\dfrac{1}{5}$        c)   $6\dfrac{1}{3}$

---

MB-25.

At the supermarket Alex can buy five sodas for $1.30. Which of the following proportions can you use to find how much eight sodas should cost? Copy and label each ratio with "$" and "sodas" to be sure the ratio on the left is consistent with the ratio on the right.

a)   $\dfrac{5}{1.30} = \dfrac{8}{C}$        b)   $\dfrac{5}{1.30} = \dfrac{C}{8}$

c)   $\dfrac{1.30}{5} = \dfrac{C}{8}$        d)   $\dfrac{5}{8} = \dfrac{1.30}{C}$

**MB-26.**  Which number makes the proportion $\frac{9}{15} = \frac{x}{20}$ true?

(A) 3          (B) 10          (C) 12          (D) 14

**MB-27.** Evaluate the following expressions:

a)    $-3 + 7 \cdot 2$        b)    $-3 \cdot 7 + (-2)$        c)    $-5 \cdot 4 + (-2) \cdot (-4)$

d)    $-3 + 7 + (-2)(-2\frac{1}{2})$    e)    $45 - (-9) + (-8)(1\frac{1}{2})$    f)    $-3 - [-2(3 + 63 \div 9)]$

**MB-28.** Complete the ratio table below to find the least common multiple of 5 and 9.

**MB-29.** **Algebra Puzzles** Solve each equation.

a)    $99w + 1 = 1$            b)    $4x - 5 = -3$

c)    $78y + 3 = -75$         d)    $7z + 5 = -5$

**MB-30.** Complete the following Diamond Problems.

Product

Sum

a)        b)        c)        d)        e)

**MB-31.** Follow your teacher's directions for practicing mental math.

**MB-32.** Deborah is going to visit her grandparents in American Samoa. She has $200 to use as spending money. If one U.S. dollar is equal to 174.94 Samoan pesetas, write and solve a proportion to find how many pesetas Deborah will have. Refer to problem MB-18 if you need help getting started.

MB-33.   Five pounds of fertilizer is needed for 1000 square feet of garden. Some students used proportions to decide how much fertilizer should be used in a 400 square foot garden.

a)   Alex wrote $\dfrac{5 \text{ lbs}}{1000 \text{ ft}^2} = \dfrac{n \text{ lbs}}{400 \text{ ft}^2}$. Solve his proportion.

b)   Taylor wrote a proportion that looked different: $\dfrac{400 \text{ sq. ft}}{x \text{ lbs}} = \dfrac{1000 \text{ sq. ft}}{5 \text{ lbs}}$.
      Solve his proportion.

c)   James wrote his proportion in another way: $\dfrac{5 \text{ lbs}}{x \text{ lbs}} = \dfrac{1000 \text{ ft}^2}{400 \text{ ft}^2}$.
      Solve this proportion.

d)   Whose proportion is correct?

e)   Jordan said, "Mine looks almost like yours, but I got a different answer." Copy and solve Jordan's proportion (at right) for y.   $\dfrac{400}{y} = \dfrac{5}{1000}$

f)   Notice that Jordan left the labels off his numbers. Write in the abbreviations "lbs" and "ft²" by his four numbers.

g)   Write a short note to Jordan describing what he needs to do to correct the way he set up his proportion. You should also comment on whether his answer is reasonable.


MB-34.   If you continued using the pattern shown at right, How many dots would you need to fill this page? Complete the questions below to help you find out.

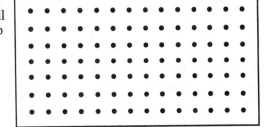

a)   How many dots are in this rectangle?

b)   Measure the rectangle to find its area in square inches.

c)   Measure the dimensions of this page to the nearest half inch. How many square inches of paper are on this page of your math book?

d)   Use the information from parts (a), (b), and (c) to find out how many dots it would take to cover the whole page using this pattern of dots.

MB-35. Janna is a painting contractor who gets many jobs painting apartments. Janna can paint a standard two-bedroom apartment in three hours.

a) How many hours will it take Janna to paint 35 standard two-bedroom apartments? Write and solve a proportion. Make sure you write your answer in a complete sentence.

b) She needs to tell the owner of the building how many days it will take her to complete the job. How many 8-hour workdays will she need? Show your work.

c) How many 5-day workweeks does that represent?

MB-36. The Reed family has decided to drive from Columbus, Ohio to Mexico City. They can travel 550 miles driving 10 hours in a day.

a) How many hours will they need to drive if the total distance is 2260 miles? Write and solve a proportion. Write your answer as a complete sentence.

b) How many 10-hour driving days will they need? Write your answer as a complete sentence.

MB-37. Solve these proportions.

a) $\dfrac{5 \text{ hot dogs}}{\$4.60} = \dfrac{8 \text{ hot dogs}}{\$C}$

b) $\dfrac{3 \text{ inches}}{96 \text{ miles}} = \dfrac{M \text{ inches}}{8 \text{ miles}}$

c) $\dfrac{54 \text{ miles}}{60 \text{ minutes}} = \dfrac{75.6 \text{ miles}}{n \text{ minutes}}$

d) $\dfrac{W \text{ words}}{8 \text{ seconds}} = \dfrac{150 \text{ words}}{120 \text{ seconds}}$

e) Choose one of the problems from parts (a) through (d) and write a word problem for the proportion shown.

MB-38. Answer these questions about big numbers.

a) How many thousands are in one million?

b) How many millions are in one billion?

c) How many billions are in one trillion?

d) Describe the pattern you see.

MB-39. Here are some questions about IMAX® films that you can solve with proportions.

a) The frames of IMAX® film are 70 millimeters wide and are projected onto a screen that is up to 99 feet wide. If a 4-millimeter long ant walked onto the film and was projected, how wide would the ant appear on a 99-foot wide screen?

b) One and one-half minutes of IMAX® film weighs 5 pounds. How much does the film for a 40-minute movie weigh?

c) The film goes through the projector at 1440 frames per 0.5 minute. How many frames go through the projector in a 40-minute film?

d) Each frame is 1.65 inches long. Use your answer from part (c) to calculate the length of the movie in miles.

MB-40. Set up and use a ratio table to find the least common multiple of 7 and 11.

MB-41. Suppose you are looking at a map on which 2 inches represents 16 miles. How many inches represent 12 miles?

(A) $1\frac{3}{8}$       (B) $1\frac{1}{2}$       (C) $1\frac{5}{8}$       (D) $2\frac{1}{4}$

MB-42. **Algebra Puzzles**

Solve each equation below. Be sure to show your work. Use the example to help you get started.

Example:

$$\frac{6y + 8}{11} = -2$$
$$6y + 8 = -22$$
$$6y = -30$$
$$y = -5$$

Check:

$$\frac{6(-5) + 8}{11} = -2$$

a) $\dfrac{7w + 3}{6} = -10$

b) $\dfrac{x - 6}{5} - 8 = -1$

MB-43. Answer the questions below.

a) Write the largest possible fraction which has a two-digit numerator and a three-digit denominator.

b) Write the smallest possible fraction which has a two-digit numerator and a three-digit denominator.

c) Write each fraction from parts (a) and (b) as a decimal.

MB-44. One place we use ratios is recording probabilities. You may recall from previous math courses that the probability or likelihood that an event will occur can be expressed as a ratio where the number of ways the event can occur is the first number and the total number of possible outcomes is the second number. For example, a bag of marbles contains 7 red marbles and 4 blue marbles, 11 marbles in all. The probability of taking out one red marble at random without looking can be written as $\frac{7}{11}$.

Linda is at the bottom of the Grand Canyon. She knows that three canoes and nine rafts will go by in the next few hours.

a) What is the probability that the first craft will be a raft?

b) What is the probability that the first craft will be a canoe?

MB-45. How many pages of newspaper do you think you need to have one million printed symbols (letters, numbers, and other printed characters)? Write down your guess.

You will now use proportions to decide more accurately.

a) Procedure.

i) Obtain a page of a newspaper and a centimeter cube from your teacher. You will work on only one side of the sheet of newspaper.

ii) With a partner, take turns rolling your cube on the page of newspaper. Trace around the cube to outline a square centimeter. Do this five times each to make a total of ten centimeter squares.

iii) Count the number of symbols inside each square centimeter. If a symbol is more than half in the square, count it. Record the number of symbols in a table like the one below.

| Roll | Number of Symbols in a Square Centimeter | Roll | Number of Symbols in a Square Centimeter |
|------|------------------------------------------|------|------------------------------------------|
| 1    |                                          | 6    |                                          |
| 2    |                                          | 7    |                                          |
| 3    |                                          | 8    |                                          |
| 4    |                                          | 9    |                                          |
| 5    |                                          | 10   |                                          |

b) Find the mean number of symbols in a square centimeter on your page of newspaper. Show your work.

c) Calculate the number of square centimeters on your page of newspaper.

d) Use your answers from (b) and (c) to set up and solve the proportion to find a total number of symbols on your page of newspaper.

e) Now that you know how many symbols are on your page of newspaper, how many pages (just like yours) would you need to have one million printed symbols? Use a proportion.

f) Compare your results for part (e) with the other teams' results. If you have to wait for the other teams to finish, do parts (i) and (j) now.

| Team Number | Pages Needed to Have 1,000,000 Symbols | Team Number | Pages Needed to Have 1,000,000 Symbols |
|---|---|---|---|
| 1 | | 6 | |
| 2 | | 7 | |
| 3 | | 8 | |
| 4 | | 9 | |
| 5 | | 10 | |

g) Find the mean number of pages your class needs to have one million symbols. Show your work.

h) Use a proportion and show your work. How many pages would your class need to make:

   i) one <u>billion</u> (1,000,000,000) symbols?

   ii) one <u>trillion</u> (1,000,000,000,000) symbols?

i) If a team only needed a few pages to get a million symbols, what do you know about their page; that is, what would it look like?

j) Suppose that 1000 pieces of sand lined up is one foot long.

   i) How long would 1,000,000 pieces of sand be?

   ii) How long would one billion pieces of sand be?

   iii) How long would one trillion pieces of sand be?

   iv) One mile is 5280 feet. Use proportions to convert your answers for (ii) and (iii) to miles.

MB-46. Use the exchange rates provided by your teacher to convert each of the following quantities into U.S. dollars.

a) 844.50 Hungarian Forints         b) 465.75 Pakistani Rupees

c) 91.65 Thai Bahts

MB-47.    A Boeing 747 airplane can travel 2470 miles from New York City to Los Angeles in about
4.75 hours.  How long would it take for the same plane to travel from Los Angeles to
Tokyo, a distance of about 5475 miles?  Write and solve a proportion.

MB-48.

> ## CONVERTING FRACTIONS TO DECIMALS
>
> Think of a fraction as a part of something.  $\frac{3}{4}$ would be three parts of 4.  To write $\frac{3}{4}$
> as a decimal, consider the fraction as a division problem:  $3 \div 4$ and perform long
> division.
>
> $$4\overline{)3.00} \quad .75$$
> $$-28$$
> $$20$$
> $$-20$$
>
> $$\frac{3}{4} = 0.75$$
>
> Sometimes the decimal number ends, and sometimes it repeats.  If it repeats, you will
> need to use bar notation.

Answer the questions below in your Tool Kit to the right of the double-lined box.

a)    Convert $\frac{1}{5}$ to a decimal.          b)    Convert $\frac{2}{3}$ to a decimal.

MB-49.    Alex needs to buy fertilizer for the school lawn.  He is supposed to use
5 pounds per 1000 square feet of lawn.  He needs to know how much           $\frac{5}{1000} = \frac{350}{x}$
fertilizer to apply on 350 square feet of lawn.  Alex wrote the
proportion at right.

a)    Solve his proportion for x.

b)    Not only can the school not afford that much fertilizer, but it would also certainly kill
the lawn.  What did he do incorrectly?

c)    What can you do to be sure you do not make the same mistake that Alex did?

d)    Set up a correct proportion and solve it.

CHAPTER 6

**MB-50.** In some of the following problems, a mistake was made. Find the mistake and explain what it is, then finish each problem correctly. If the problem is correct, write "Correct."

a) $(3 + 2) \cdot (8 - 12)$

$$\boxed{(3 + 2)} \cdot \boxed{(8 - 12)}$$

$$5 \cdot \text{-4}$$

$$\text{-20}$$

b) $2 \cdot 10 + (68 \div 17 \cdot 2)$

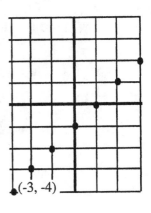

$$\boxed{2 \cdot 10} + \boxed{(68 \div 17 \cdot 2)}$$

$$20 + 4 \cdot 2$$

$$24 \cdot 2$$

$$48$$

c) $\dfrac{2(16 - 2)}{14} + 2 \cdot 8$

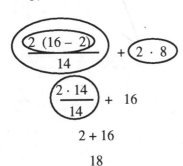

$$\boxed{\dfrac{2 \ (16 - 2)}{14}} + \boxed{2 \cdot 8}$$

$$\boxed{\dfrac{2 \cdot 14}{14}} + 16$$

$$2 + 16$$

$$18$$

d) 
$$2 + 16 \div 2 \cdot 8$$
$$18 \div 2 \cdot 8$$
$$9 \cdot 8$$
$$72$$

**MB-51.** Below you see a graph of seven coordinate points.

a) Look at the points in the graph and write them in a table to organize them.

Example:

| x | -3 | -2 | -1 | 0 | 1 | 2 | 3 |
|---|----|----|----|---|---|---|---|
| y | -4 |    |    |   |   |   |   |

b) What algebraic rule created these points?

c) Name at least two other points which would follow this rule.

(-3, -4)

**MB-52.** Which sentence is true?

(A) $\dfrac{4}{7} = \dfrac{6}{8}$  (B) $\dfrac{2}{5} = \dfrac{3}{10}$  (C) $\dfrac{2}{3} = \dfrac{3}{4}$  (D) $\dfrac{3}{9} = \dfrac{1}{3}$

MB-53.  Follow your teacher's directions for practicing mental math.

MB-54.  Solve these proportions.

a)  $\dfrac{70}{100} = \dfrac{56 \text{ points}}{x \text{ total points}}$

b)  $\dfrac{T}{100} = \dfrac{\$1.60}{\$32}$

c)  $\dfrac{19 \text{ points earned}}{76 \text{ points total}} = \dfrac{Y}{100}$

d)  $\dfrac{15}{100} = \dfrac{w}{\$56.00}$

e)  Choose one of the problems from parts (a) through (d) and write a word problem for the proportion shown.

MB-55.  Complete the following ratio tables.

a)

| 4 | 8 | 10 | 20 |    | 60 |     |
|---|---|----|----|----|----|-----|
| 5 |   |    |    | 50 |    | 100 |

b)

| 3  | 15 |    | 30 |    | 150 |     |
|----|----|----|----|----|-----|-----|
| 4  |    | 24 |    | 48 |     | 100 |

c)

| 0.55 | 1.10 | 2.20 |   |    |    |     |
|------|------|------|---|----|----|-----|
| 0.50 |      |      | 5 | 10 | 50 | 100 |

MB-56.  Ratio tables can be used to calculate percents.  Use the tables in the preceding problem to compute these percents.

a)  Fred got his last math test back and found that he answered four out of every five questions correctly.  Fred wants to know his grade as a percent.  Use the ratio table in part (a) of the previous problem to find Fred's grade.  Remember that percent means "out of 100."

b)  On the same test, Wilma answered three out of every four questions correctly.  Use one of the ratio tables in the previous problem to determine Wilma's percentage.  How did you decide which ratio table to use?

c)  Giant gumballs from a machine cost 50 cents.  Jeddie paid Elvis 55 cents for a gumball.  What percent of the original price did he pay?

MB-57.  Each of the three previous problems involve percents.  In each case we were interested in finding some quantity out of 100.  Using ratio tables is one method for finding percents, but proportions are often more efficient.  For example, we can write the proportion
$\dfrac{4 \text{ questions correct}}{5 \text{ questions total}} = \dfrac{x \text{ correct}}{100 \text{ total}}$ to find Fred's percent correct.  We know that Fred has 80 questions correct out of 100 questions.  This means that Fred scored 80% on his test.

Write and solve a proportion to find Wilma's percentage of correct answers.

MB-58.    Jamal wants to calculate the tip on the lunch he has just eaten.  His bill is $4.98, and he wants to leave a 15% tip.  Because Jamal knows that 15% means "15 out of 100" he writes the following proportion:

$$\frac{15}{100} = \frac{\$x \text{ tip}}{\$4.98 \text{ total}}$$

Use complete sentences to answer each of the following questions.

a)    Why does Jamal write $\frac{15}{100}$ ?

b)    Why is $4.98 in the <u>denominator</u> of the second fraction?

c)    Why is $x in the <u>numerator</u> of the second fraction?

d)    Solve the proportion.

e)    How much money will Jamal leave as the tip?  Write your answer as a complete sentence.

MB-59.    Write and solve a proportion for part (a), then complete parts (b) and (c).

a)    Balvina wants to buy a new chair.  She has found one that she really likes, and it is marked down 25% from the original price of $140.  How much will she save if she buys the chair?

b)    What is the sale price of Balvina's chair?

c)    Write a proportion to find 75% of $140.

d)    Explain why the answers for parts (b) and (c) are the same.

MB-60.   On this map, 4 inches represents 5 miles.  Write and solve a proportion to find the actual distances in miles.

Grizzly Peak

Liberty Camp

Emerald Pool

Vernal Fall

Trail
Mist

Merced River

Nevada Fall

John Muir Trail

a)   On the map the distance from Vernal Fall to Nevada Fall is $1\frac{7}{8}$ inches. What is the actual distance?

b)   On the map the distance from Grizzly Peak to Vernal Fall is $1\frac{3}{8}$ inches. What is the actual distance?

c)   On the map the distance from Grizzly Peak to Liberty Camp is $3\frac{1}{8}$ inches. What is the actual distance?

MB-61.   Solve the following percent questions using proportions.

a)   If you get 23 out of 25 points on a quiz, what is your score as a percent?

b)   If you want at least 80% on a 60 point quiz, how many points do you need to earn?

c)   If your friend got 73% and earned 46 points, how many points was the quiz worth?

MB-62.   This information was collected during the 2000 Census.  Write and solve a proportion for each question.

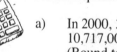

a)   In 2000, 31.6% of the population of California was Latino.  There were about 10,717,000 Latinos in the state.  What was the total population of California? (Round to the nearest thousand.)

b)   There were 72,294,000 children under the age of 18 out of 284 million total Americans.  What percent of the total population was under the age of 18?

c)   New York had 6.7% of the total U.S. population in 2000.  How many people lived in New York if there were 284,000,000 people in the U.S.?

MB-63.   Percents are frequently used for monetary calculations. Write and solve a proportion to answer each of the following questions.

a)   Banks will pay you money (interest) if you keep your money in their bank. How much interest will Shan earn if a bank offers him 6% to keep his $250 there for a year?

b)   Stores often discount products during sales. How much money do you save if you buy a $54 pair of shoes for 20% off? What will be the sale price after the discount?

c)   If you have good service in a restaurant, it is common to leave a 15% to 20% tip for the food server. How much of a tip will Adam leave if his meal costs $24.50 and he leaves exactly a 20% tip? What is the total price of his meal and tip?

MB-64.

---

### PERCENTS USING PROPORTIONS

- Proportions can be used to find percents.

- Set up your proportion with the percent numbers on one side and the quantities you wish to compare on the other side.

  Example: What number is 15% of 140?

  $$\frac{\text{part} \rightarrow 15}{\text{whole} \rightarrow 100} = \frac{x}{140}$$

- Cross multiply to write an equation without fractions.

  $$15 \cdot 140 = 100x$$

- Solve for the unknown.

  $$x = 21$$

---

a)   Make these notes in your Tool Kit to the right of the double-lined box. Highlight the example given in the Tool Kit entry.

b)   Why is the answer a reasonable one for this problem?

MB-65.   The average television program has one minute of commercials for every four minutes of actual programming. If you turn on the television at a random time, what is the probability that the TV will come on with a commercial? Write your answer as a percent.

MB-66.   A jar contains 15 licorice jelly beans and 35 cherry jelly beans. If you pick a jelly bean at random out of the jar, what is the probability that you will get a licorice jelly bean? Write your answer as a percent.

MB-67. Complete the ratio table below to find the least common multiple of 6 and 8.

a)

$$\frac{6}{8}$$ |——|——|——|——|——|——|——|

b)    What is the least common multiple of 6 and 8?

MB-68.  **Algebra Puzzles**  Solve each equation. Show your work.

a)    $\frac{7 - 9c}{10} = 7$

b)    $17 + \frac{8w - 3}{9} = 22$

MB-69. One way to find 28% of 105 is:

(A) $0.28 + 105$        (B) $105 - 0.28$        (C) $0.28(105)$        (D) $105 \div 0.28$

MB-70. Find $\frac{3}{2} \cdot \frac{4}{3} \cdot \frac{5}{4} \cdot \frac{6}{5} \cdot \dots \cdot \frac{21}{20}$.

MB-71. A person who weighs 100 pounds on Earth would weigh about 38 pounds on Mars.

a)    Find the Mars weight of a student who weighs 150 pounds on Earth.

b)    Find the Earth weight of a student who weighs 40 pounds on Mars.

c)    Find the approximate weight of your backpack on Mars.

MB-72.    Proportions are a great tool for finding percentages, but frequently you need to estimate a percent quickly. For example, if you are calculating a tip or deciding if a sale item is affordable, you need a mental math technique for finding percents.

a)    Here are some examples of 10% of an amount:

- 10% of $35.00 is $3.50.
- 10% of $7.20 is $0.72.
- 10% of $920,000 is $92,000.

What do you notice about 10% of a number?

b)    Find 10% of $560.00.                    c)    Find 10% of $9.00.

d)    Here are some examples of 1% of an amount:

- 1% of $35.00 is $0.35.
- 1% of $7.20 is $0.072.
- 1% of $920,000 is $9200.

What do you notice about 1% of a number?

e)    Find 1% of $560.00.                    f)    Find 1% of $9.00.


MB-73.    Use your knowledge of how to find 10% and 1% of an amount to choose the correct answer for each of the following problems. Do not calculate the answers, just estimate them.

a)    Mrs. Poppington based her semester grades on a total of 576 points. Clark had 73% of the points. Was that 42, 4204, or 420 points?

b)    The sales tax rate is 7.5%. On a $257 bicycle, would the tax be $192.75, $19.28, or $72.40?

c)    Would a 15% tip on a bill for $48.27 be $7.24, $0.72, or $72.40?

d)    The tax in another town is 8.25%. Would the amount of tax on a $15,780 car be $13.01, $130.18, $1301.85, or $13,018.50?


MB-74.    The **unit price** is the cost of one unit of an item. Suppose a 16 oz. bottle of shampoo costs $3.68. One way to find the unit price is to write a proportion that has 1 ounce as one part of the proportion.

Example: $\dfrac{\$3.68}{16 \text{ oz}} = \dfrac{\$x}{1 \text{ oz}}$

Solving the proportion gives x = $0.23, so the shampoo costs $0.23 per oz.

a)    Find the unit price of *Italy* brand olive oil, which costs $2.90 for 10 ounces.

b)    Find the unit price of *Delicious* brand olive oil, which costs $4.96 for 16 ounces.

c)    If both brands are of the same quality, which one is the better buy?

MB-75.  The **unit rate** is a rate with a denominator of 1. From a sprinter's time of 10.49 seconds in the 100 m dash, we can find her speed per second or we can find the number of seconds she takes for one meter.

Example: $\frac{100 \text{ m}}{10.49 \text{ sec}} = \frac{x \text{ m}}{1 \text{ sec}}$ gives $x = 9.53$, so she

ran 9.53 meters each second.

OR $\frac{10.49 \text{ sec}}{100 \text{ m}} = \frac{x \text{ sec}}{1 \text{ m}}$ gives $x = 0.1049$, so

it took her 0.1049 seconds to run each meter.

a) An ice skater covered 1500 m in 106.43 seconds. Find his unit rate of speed in meters per second.

b) A train in Japan can travel 813.5 miles in 5 hours. Find the unit rate of speed in miles per hour.

c) Alaska has a very low population density. It only has 604,000 people in 570,374 square miles. Find the unit rate of density in terms of people per square mile.

d) New Jersey has a high population density. It has 1,071 people per square mile. If Alaska had the same population density as New Jersey, what would be the population of Alaska? Solve with a proportion. (By the way, there were about 284,000,000 people in the United States as of the year 2000.)

MB-76.  We know that 10% of a number can be calculated mentally by dividing by 10 or moving the decimal one place to the left. Other percents can be calculated mentally once you know 10%. Start each problem by calculating 10%. Be ready to explain your method.

a) Mentally calculate 20% of $40.     b) Mentally calculate 5% of $40.

c) Mentally calculate 15% of $40.     d) Mentally calculate 30% of $40.

MB-77. A store in the mall is having a 30%-off sale.

a) Write and solve a proportion to find the discount on a pair of pants that is normally $79.

b) What is the sale price of the pants?

c) If the pants are not on sale, then you pay 100% of the price. However, if the store takes off 30%, what percent of the normal price do you pay?

d) Calculate 70% of the normal $79 pants price.

e) Compare your answers from part (b) and part (d).

f) The first technique used to find sale prices in this problem was to calculate 30% of the normal price and then subtract that amount from the original price. The second technique was to find 70% of the normal price. Which method do you prefer? Explain.

MB-78.   Solve these percent problems.

   a)   60% of the box at right is not shaded.  What percent is shaded?

   b)   Oil provides 39.7% of the world's energy.  What percent of the
        world's energy comes from other sources?

   c)   95% of the people bitten by a Black Mamba snake in Africa die from the venom.
        What is the survival rate for people bitten by the Black Mamba snake in Africa?


MB-79.   Practice your mental math abilities with these problems.  Do not use a proportion and

         do not use a calculator.

   a)   Mentally calculate 20% of $62.        b)   Mentally calculate 30% of $62.

   c)   Mentally calculate 15% of $62.        d)   Mentally calculate 50% of $62.

   e)   Mentally calculate 55% of $62.

   f)   In part (d) did you use parts (a) and (b) or did you just remember that 50%
        means $\frac{1}{2}$ ?


MB-80.   Find the sale price for these items.  Use the method from problem MB-77 that you prefer.

   a)   A pair of shoes that normally costs $75.50 goes on sale for 40% off.

   b)   A jacket that normally costs $52.75 goes on sale for 15% off.

   c)   A book that normally costs $18.50 goes on sale for 25% off.


MB-81.   The scale drawing at right shows the first floor
         of a house.  The actual dimensions of the
         garage are 20 feet by 25 feet.  All angles are
         right angles.

   a)   How many feet does each inch represent?

   b)   What is the length and width of the living
        room in inches?

   c)   What is the length and width of the living
        room in feet?

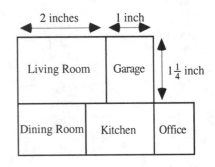

   d)   If the family wants to carpet the living room and carpeting costs $1.25 per square
        foot, how much will the carpet cost?

   e)   What is the perimeter of the garage (in feet)?

MB-82.    Use your ruler to verify that for the scale shown on the map, $1\frac{3}{8}$ inches represents 0.5 miles.

a)    What is the distance from Sentinel Fall to Sentinel Dome in inches?

b)    Convert your answer from part (a) into a decimal.

c)    Write and solve a proportion to calculate the distance in miles from Sentinel Fall to Sentinel Dome.

MB-83.    Here is a graphical look at proportions and percents. You will do problems like this for the rest of the course. Your solution should include a sketch of each graph, the problem in words, a proportion that includes a variable, and an answer. The first problem has been completed for you as a model.

| Picture | Problem in Words / Proportion | Answer |
|---|---|---|
| 75 ⌐⌐ 100%<br>n ⌐ 80%<br><br>0 ⌐ 0% | What is 80% of 75?<br><br>$\frac{80}{100} = \frac{n}{75}$ | n = 60 |
| n ⌐100%<br><br>20 ⌐ 40%<br><br>0 ⌐0% | State the question in words.<br><br>———— = ————<br><br>Write a proportion. | |

MB-84.    Find the value of each absolute value expression.

a)    $|-13| - |13|$                     b)    $|-19| - |-17|$

c)    $|-16|$                     d)    $|4|$

**MB-85.** There are 100 candies in a jar. If 48% are chocolate, how many candies are <u>not</u> chocolate?

(A) 48            (B) 52            (C) 0.48            (D) 100

**MB-86.** Photocopiers commonly enlarge or reduce images. If you enlarge or reduce all the dimensions of a geometric figure equally, the resulting figure is called a **similar** figure. Based on the appearance of each of the following examples, write "similar" or "not similar."

a)
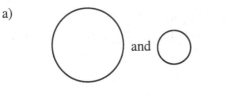

b)
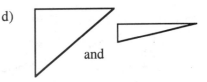

c)
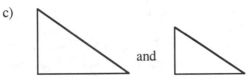

d)
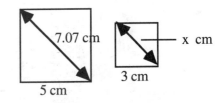

**MB-87.** One important property of similar shapes is that their corresponding side lengths and diagonals are in proportion to each other. This makes it possible to find missing side lengths when we know the shapes are similar. The two squares at right are similar. Use a proportion to find the length of the diagonal of the smaller square.

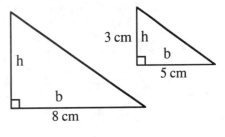

$$\underbrace{\frac{\text{side}}{\text{diagonal}}}_{\textbf{Big Square}} = \underbrace{\frac{\text{side}}{\text{diagonal}}}_{\textbf{Small Square}}$$

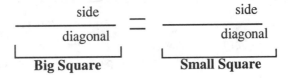

**MB-88.** The two triangles at right are similar. In each one, h is the height and b is the base. Write a proportion and solve it for the height of the larger triangle.

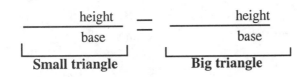

$$\underbrace{\frac{\text{height}}{\text{base}}}_{\textbf{Small triangle}} = \underbrace{\frac{\text{height}}{\text{base}}}_{\textbf{Big triangle}}$$

MB-89. The rays of the sun shining on a vertical object form a right triangle with the object and its shadow. If two objects are close together, like the girl and the tree shown at right, the triangles will be similar because the angles of the sun's rays are the same. We can use similar triangles to find the height of the tree without actually measuring the tree itself. Use the information in the drawing to set up a proportion to find the height of the tree.

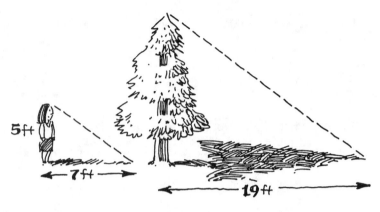

MB-90. Write a proportion to solve for the missing lengths in each pair of similar figures.

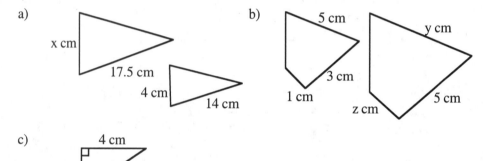

a)

x cm

17.5 cm

4 cm

14 cm

b)

5 cm

y cm

3 cm

1 cm

5 cm

z cm

c)

4 cm

3 cm

5 cm

p cm

q cm

27 cm

MB-91. Create a table to organize a set of points for the rule $y = \frac{x \cdot x}{2}$. Use at least three negative x-values in your table. Plot the ordered pairs on a coordinate graph.

MB-92. Samy has decided to sell a jacket in his store for $75. The original price of the jacket was $125.

a) Write and solve a proportion to find what percent $75 is of $125.

b) What is the discount amount in dollars?

c) What percent of the original cost is the discounted amount?

MB-93.  Find the value of each absolute value expression.

a)  $|28| - |47|$

b)  $|19| - |-15|$

c)  $|-45| + |16|$

d)  $|-18|$

MB-94.  Find the least common multiple for each of the following pairs of integers.

a)  4 and 7

b)  6 and 10

c)  10 and 18

MB-95.  There are three red marbles, two orange marbles, and five blue marbles in a bag. What is the probability of pulling an orange marble from the bag?

(A) 20%

(B) 30%

(C) 50%

(D) 23%

MB-96.  **Algebra Puzzles**  Decide which number belongs in the place of the variable to make the equation true.

a)  $3w + 1 = 3$

b)  $4x - 5 = 1$

c)  $2y + 3 = 11$

d)  $7z + 5 = 2$

MB-97.  We changed the water in our fish tank and needed to add a little acid to bring the water to the right pH. We did not have a tool to measure pH, but our neighbor had a kit for his pool and told us that if our aquarium held 10,000 gallons of water, we would need to add 4 gallons of acid. However, our aquarium only holds 6 gallons of water. How many teaspoons of acid do we need? Note: There are 48 teaspoons in one 8-ounce cup.

MB-98.  Complete the following Diamond Problems.

Product

Sum

a)

b)

c)

d)

e)

MB-99. **Solar System Model Project**

Your team will assemble one of the models of the solar system shown below. Each team member needs to show the proportions used to create the model. Solar system data is provided in the table below right.

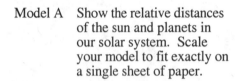

Your model will be graded on:
- use of the assigned scale.
- clearly shown proportions.
- correct calculations.
- appearance of model.

For *Models A through D*: Model relative distances. Label the location of each planet. Do not build a model of the planet.

| Object | Mean Distance from the Sun (km) | Mean Diameter (km) |
|--------|---------------------------------|--------------------|
| Mercury | 59,840,000 | 4878 |
| Venus | 104,720,000 | 12,104 |
| Earth | 149,600,000 | 12,756 |
| Mars | 209,440,000 | 6796 |
| Jupiter | 777,920,000 | 142,984 |
| Saturn | 1,436,160,000 | 120,536 |
| Uranus | 2,872,320,000 | 51,118 |
| Neptune | 4,502,960,000 | 49,528 |
| Pluto | 5,894,240,000 | 2,302 |
| Sun | — | 1,391,000 |

Model A   Show the relative distances of the sun and planets in our solar system. Scale your model to fit exactly on a single sheet of paper.

Model B   Show the relative distances of the sun and planets in our solar system. Scale your model to fit on the combined desks of all team members.

Model C   Show the relative distances of the sun and planets in our solar system. Scale your model to fit exactly within this classroom.

Model D   Show the relative distances of the sun and planets in our solar system. Scale your model to fit within a location outside designated by your teacher.

For *Models E through H*: Model relative planet size. "Planets" can be various balls, or you can easily make planet models by wadding scrap paper into a ball and securing it with tape. In some of the models, planets would be so large it would not be practical to create a spherical model for the planet. Instead, model the length of the diameter of the planet.

Model E   Show the relative sizes of the sun and planets in our solar system. Scale your model so that the largest planet is the size of a softball.

Model F   Show the relative sizes of the sun and planets in our solar system. Scale your model so that the largest planet is the size of a soccer ball.

Model G   Show the relative sizes of the sun and planets in our solar system. Scale your model so that the largest planet is as tall as the tallest person in your study team.

Model H   Show the relative sizes of the sun and planets in our solar system. Scale your model so that the largest planet is the height of this classroom.

MB-100. Solve these proportions.

a) $\dfrac{16 \text{ red candies}}{38 \text{ total}} = \dfrac{N \text{ red candies}}{450 \text{ total}}$

b) $\dfrac{16 \text{ red candies}}{38 \text{ total}} = \dfrac{200 \text{ red candies}}{M \text{ total}}$

c) $\dfrac{19 \text{ boys}}{30 \text{ total students}} = \dfrac{V \text{ boys}}{490 \text{ total students}}$

d) $\dfrac{19 \text{ boys}}{x \text{ total students}} = \dfrac{175 \text{ boys}}{490 \text{ total students}}$

e) Choose one of the problems from parts (a) through (d) and write a word problem for the proportion shown.

MB-101. Here is a graphical look at proportions and percents. Copy and complete the table.

| Picture | Problem in Words / Proportion | Answer |
|---|---|---|
| 24 — 100% <br> n — 5% <br> 0 — 0% | What is 5% of 24? <br><br> ——— = ——— | |
| 60 — 100% <br> 22.5 — n% <br> 0 — 0% | State the question in words. <br><br> ——— = ——— | |

MB-102. Seventeen out of 20 is what percent?

    (A) 17%         (B) 20%         (C) 85%         (D) 97%

MB-103. Julie scored 136 out of 200 on her midterm. Write and solve a proportion that will give you Julie's percentage.

MB-104. Find the least common multiple for each of the following pairs of integers.

a)   3 and 8

b)   4 and 13

c)   18 and 12

MB-105. Evaluate each expression.

a)   $-8 + 7 \cdot 2$

b)   $-3 \cdot (-7) + (-2)$

c)   $-5 \cdot (-4) \div 2 - (-4)$

d)   $-3 + 7 + (-2)(-4\frac{1}{2})$

e)   $25 - (-9) + (-4)(1\frac{1}{4})$

f)   $(-3)(-3) - (-2\frac{1}{3}(-8 + 72 \div 9))$

MB-106. **Algebra Puzzles**  Solve each equation.

a)   $3w + 1 = -1$

b)   $7z + 5 = -12$

c)   $-1 = 3 + 2y$

d)   $5 - 4x = 7$

MB-107. Cardenas reached into his pocket to tip the porter.  He had just arrived in England and knew he had 10 U.S. dollar bills and 20 British pound notes crumpled in his pocket.  What is the probability of his pulling out a pound note?

MB-108. **The Solar System Presentations**

Today you will do your presentations of the solar system models you built with your team.

MB-109. One model for dividing negative numbers is to think of tile spacers.  Here, for example, is -6 divided into two groups with -3 in each group:

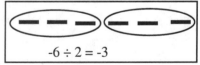

$-6 \div 2 = -3$

a)   Draw the tile spacers that would represent $-8 \div 4$.

b)   Draw the tile spacers that would represent $-12 \div 4$.

c)   Draw the tile spacers that would represent $-9 \div 3$.

d)   Draw the tile spacers that would represent $10 \div 5$.

MB-110. Another way to understand dividing negative integers is to think of multiplication and division as inverse operations. For each problem write two division problems using what you know about multiplication of integers.

Example: $3 \cdot 5 = 15$, $\quad 15 \div 5 = 3$, $\quad 15 \div 3 = 5$

a) $3(4) = 12$      b) $3(-4) = -12$      c) $-3(-4) = 12$      d) $5(-4) = -20$

MB-111. Use a proportion to answer the questions below.

a) In Japan, 458 out of every 500 people own a radio. What percent of the Japanese population owns a radio?

b) In the United States, 1046 radios are owned by every 500 people. What is the unit rate for radios owned per person?

MB-112. Evaluate the following expressions.

a) $-3 - 7 \cdot 2$      b) $-3 \cdot (-8) - (-2)$      c) $5 \cdot 4 - (-16) \div (-4)$

d) $-3 \cdot 7 + 4(-2\frac{1}{2})$      e) $0 - (-1) + (-1) \div (-1)$    f) $(-3) - (2(12 + (-63) \div 9))$

MB-113. A jar contains eight red checkers and lots of black checkers. If you pick a checker randomly, without looking into the jar, the chance of getting a black checker is 60%.

a) What is the probability of getting a red checker?

b) How many checkers are in the jar?

c) How many black checkers are in the jar?

MB-114. Find the value of each of the absolute value expressions.

a) $|36| + |-10|$      b) $|-2.4| + |3.2|$      c) $|15| + |-6.2|$

MB-115. Practice your mental math abilities with these problems.

a) Mentally calculate 20% of $24.      b) Mentally calculate 30% of $24.

c) Mentally calculate 15% of $24.      d) Mentally calculate 50% of $24.

e) Mentally calculate 55% of $24.

MB-116. What is 4% written as a decimal?

(A) 4         (B) 0.4         (C) 0.04         (D) 0.004

MB-117. Sally the Stock Speculator bought $100,000 worth of stocks on February 1 and sold them for a 50% profit in June. Then she invested the money in another stock and lost 50% of that investment when she sold in September. How much did she have in September? Show all your work.

MB-118. **Chapter Summary** Writing and solving proportions has been the main focus of this chapter.

To review and summarize your work with proportions, select or create five problems that can be solved using a proportion and show how to solve each one. Be sure that at least one problem involves each of the following ideas:

- percents.
- similar geometric figures.
- scale drawing or a map.
- discount or sale price.
- finding unit rate or unit price.

MB-119. Here are some monetary percents for you to find using proportions.

a) How much money will Sydney earn if a bank offers her 6.5% simple interest to keep her $325 in the bank for a year? If she does not take any money out of her account, what will the account be worth at the end of the year?

b) How much will a store take off the price of a $19.90 shirt if they offer 40% off? What will be the sale price after the discount?

c) How much of a tip will Martin leave if his meal costs $36.60 and he leaves a15% tip? What is the total price of his meal and tip?

MB-120. Use proportions to find the missing lengths. Assume that each pair of shapes is similar, but not necessarily drawn to scale.

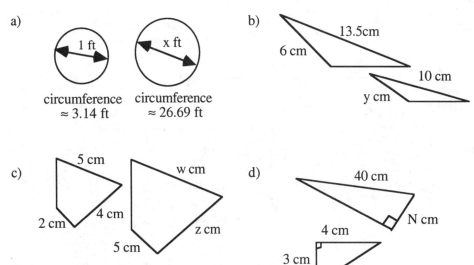

a)

circumference ≈ 3.14 ft    circumference ≈ 26.69 ft

b)

c)

d)

MB-121. A class has 8 boys and the other 68% of the class is girls.

a)   What percent of the class is boys?

b)   How many students are in the class?

c)   How many girls are in the class?

MB-122. Practice your mental math abilities with these problems.

a)   Mentally calculate 20% of $150.    b)   Mentally calculate 5% of $150.

c)   Mentally calculate 15% of $150.    d)   Mentally calculate 25% of $150.

e)   Mentally calculate 55% of $150.

MB-123. Compute the least common multiple of each pair of numbers. Use the method of your choice.

a)   4 and 20          b)   8 and 3          c)   10 and 15

MB-124. Draw a number line from -1 to 1 like the line shown below. Then write the following numbers in their correct places on the number line.

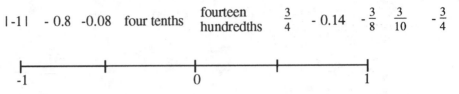

$|-1|$    $- 0.8$   $-0.08$   four tenths   fourteen hundredths   $\frac{3}{4}$   $- 0.14$   $-\frac{3}{8}$   $\frac{3}{10}$   $-\frac{3}{4}$

MB-125. You should notice some patterns regarding multiplication and division of integers. Copy and complete the following problems:

a)    $2(4)$                $-2(4)$                $4(-2)$                $-2(-4)$

b)    When you multiply two integers with the same sign, is the product positive or negative?

c)    When you multiply two integers with different signs, is the product positive or negative?

d)    Divide each pair of integers:

    $20 \div 4$            $20 \div (-4)$            $-20 \div 4$            $-20 \div (-4)$

e)    When you divide two integers with the same sign, is the quotient positive or negative?

f)    When you divide two integers with different signs, is the quotient positive or negative?

g)    Look at your answers for parts (b), (c), (e), and (f). How are the rules for multiplication and division related?

MB-126. Jameela was shopping and found a lovely coat for only $45. The tag said that the coat had been marked down 20%. Jameela wants to know the original price.

a)    Write and solve a proportion to find the original cost of the coat.

b)    If the coat is marked down to 80% of the original price, what percent has it been marked down?

c)    How much money has Jameela saved by buying the coat on sale?

MB-127. Frederick invested money in the stock market. A few months later, his wife found a statement showing that his investment was worth only $63,000, which is 70% of the original amount. How much money did Frederick invest originally? Write and solve a proportion.

MB-128. Copy each problem, solve it in your head, and write the answer.

a)    -63 ÷ 9          -63 ÷ (-9)          63 ÷ (-9)          63 ÷ 9

b)    -27 ÷ 3          -27 ÷ (-3)          27 ÷ (-3)          27 ÷ 3

c)    -64 ÷ 8          -64 ÷ (-8)          64 ÷ (-8)          64 ÷ 8

MB-129. Which of the following proportions could <u>not</u> be used to solve this problem: "Judy can walk six blocks in 9 minutes. How many blocks can she walk in 18 minutes?"

(A) $\frac{6}{9} = \frac{x}{18}$          (B) $\frac{9}{6} = \frac{18}{x}$          (C) $\frac{9}{18} = \frac{6}{x}$          (D) $\frac{18}{9} = \frac{6}{x}$

MB-130. A shirt that normally costs $35 is on sale for 25% off. What is the sale price?

(A) $26.25          (B) $8.75          (C) $43.75          (D) $28.75

MB-131. **Algebra Puzzles**  Solve these equations.

a)    $3w + 1 = 6$

b)    $-3 = 7 - 4x$

c)    $6 + 2y = -7$

d)    $7z + 5 = -19$

MB-132. Bill sells tofu hot dogs out of a cart in Yosemite Village. The tofu dogs cost Bill $1.50 each. If he sells all of them for $1.80 each, how much money will he have from his sales if he purchased $105 worth of hot dogs? Write and solve a proportion to answer this question.

MB-133. **What We Have Done in This Chapter**

Below is a list of the Tool Kit entries from this chapter.

- MB-8    Solving Proportions Using Cross Multiplication
- MB-22   Least Common Multiples
- MB-48   Converting Fractions to Decimals
- MB-64   Percents Using Proportions

Review all the entries and read the notes you made in your Tool Kit. Make a list of any questions, terms, or notes you do not understand. Ask your partner or study team members for help. If anything is still unclear, ask your teacher.

# The Garcia's New House

## Chapter 7

# Chapter 7
### *The Garcias' New House:* OPERATIONS WITH FRACTIONS AND DECIMALS

You have worked with fractions and decimals in earlier classes. This chapter provides some new ways to see why the rules for adding, subtracting, multiplying, and dividing fractions work. You will gain some insight into why common denominators are so important.

 The main goals of this chapter are for you to understand fractions and to become efficient with doing calculations with them. This is a **NO CALCULATOR** chapter. You may only use a calculator for any problem that has the "use calculator" icon.

In this chapter you will have the opportunity to:

- deepen your understanding of addition and subtraction of fractions.

- use and compare several alternative ways to add and subtract mixed numbers.

- use multiplication of fractions in contexts that illustrate how it works.

- understand the reasons for inverting the divisor when dividing fractions.

- examine the reason for counting decimal places when multiplying and "moving the decimal point" when dividing.

Read the following problem carefully, but **do not try to solve it now**. What you learn over the next few days will enable you to solve it.

GH-0.   Sandy is the contractor hired to build the Garcias' new house. She needs to frame the doorway so that the finished opening is $32\frac{1}{8}$ inches by $80\frac{1}{4}$ inches. What lengths of 2-by-4 lumber will Sandy need to cut?

| | |
|---|---|
| Number Sense | |
| Algebra and Functions | |
| Mathematical Reasoning | |
| Measurement and Geometry | |
| Statistics, Data Analysis, & Probability | |

# Chapter 7
The Garcias' New House: **OPERATIONS WITH FRACTIONS AND DECIMALS**

GH-1.  Mentally estimate each sum and write "greater than 1" or "less than 1."

a) $\frac{1}{6} + \frac{2}{3}$

b) $\frac{3}{4} + \frac{5}{6}$

c) $\frac{1}{12} + \frac{7}{8}$

GH-2. Copy this rectangular drawing of $\frac{1}{4} + \frac{1}{2}$ and fill in the missing quantities. You may shade with pencil or two colors of pen or highlighter.

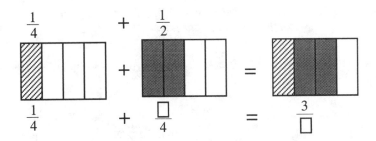

GH-3. Review the previous problem. Notice that the bottom equation was easier to solve than the top equation because it had common denominators. You learned to make common denominators in previous chapters using the Giant **1**, ratio tables, rectangular area models, and fraction bars. Below is a different way to picture fraction addition problems. Notice that the second fraction, $\frac{1}{2}$, has been drawn horizontally this time.

a) What fraction problem does this picture show?

b) Describe how the picture at right differs from the picture in part (a).

c) The picture in part (a) shows $\frac{1}{4} + \frac{1}{2}$. What does the picture in part (b) show? Write the expression using a common denominator.

d) Which of the pictures at right shows the correct solution to this problem?

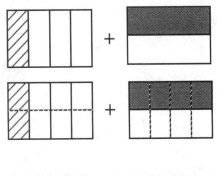

Figure A          Figure B

GH-4.    Notice how the process of superimposing one fraction diagram on the other allows us to
         see a common denominator. In the problem below the common denominator is 12
         because after superimposing one fraction on the other, there are 12 small rectangles.
         Complete the fraction equation below the figures and write the equation on your paper.

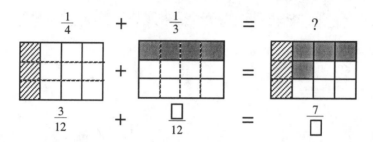

GH-5.    The process for drawing subtraction problems with fractions is similar. We will draw
         each fraction and then remove the second fraction from the first.

    a)    Copy this rectangular drawing of $\frac{2}{3} - \frac{1}{4}$ and fill in the missing quantities.

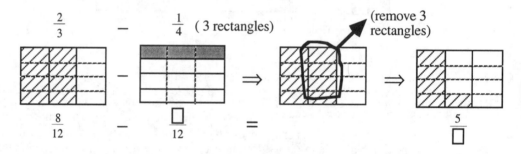

    b)    Try the next one on your own. Draw each fraction and remove the second fraction
          from the first.

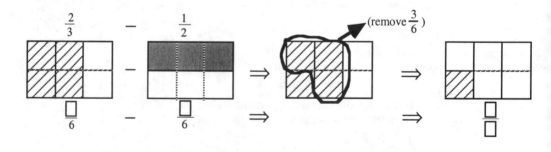

GH-6. Obtain the resource page for this problem from your teacher. As you complete parts (a) through (f) below, follow these steps:

1. Draw and shade a rectangle for each fraction. Use vertical lines for one fraction and horizontal lines for the other.

2. Add dotted lines to each drawing to get a common denominator.

3. Find the sum or difference in each problem.

a) $\frac{3}{5} + \frac{1}{4}$      b) $\frac{1}{2} + \frac{1}{3}$      c) $\frac{2}{3} + \frac{1}{4}$

d) $\frac{3}{4} - \frac{2}{3}$      e) $\frac{3}{4} - \frac{1}{3}$      f) $\frac{4}{5} - \frac{1}{2}$

GH-7. Use the rectangle drawing method to answer the questions below. Alex and Georgette bring candy to class to share. Alex brings $\frac{1}{2}$ pound of candy and Georgette brings $\frac{2}{3}$ pound.

a) How many pounds of candy do they have altogether?

b) How much more candy did Georgette bring than Alex?

GH-8. Use the method of drawing rectangles to answer the questions below. Ramona has two canteens to take on a hike across the desert. One canteen contains $\frac{1}{6}$ quart of water. The other one contains $\frac{3}{4}$ quart.

a) How much water does she have?

b) How much more water does the larger canteen contain than the smaller canteen?

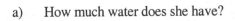

GH-9. Ashlyn has planted one-third of her garden with beans and one-fifth with lettuce.

a) How much of the garden has she planted?

b) How much more of the garden is planted with beans than with lettuce?

GH-10. Solve these proportions.

a) $\dfrac{1{,}900{,}000 \text{ miles}}{1.9 \text{ cm}} = \dfrac{500{,}000 \text{ miles}}{N \text{ cm}}$

b) $\dfrac{5 \text{ cm}}{1{,}900{,}000 \text{ miles}} = \dfrac{4 \text{ cm}}{Z \text{ miles}}$

c) Choose one of the problems above and write a word problem for the proportion shown.

GH-11. Find the area of each triangle.

a)

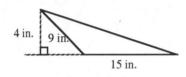

4 in.  9 in.  15 in.

b)

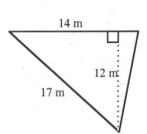

14 m  12 m  17 m

GH–12. Find each of the following.

a) $|\text{-}55| + |\text{-}44|$

b) $|\text{-}15| - |18|$

c) $|\text{-}\tfrac{2}{3}| + |\tfrac{5}{6}|$

d) $|33| - |\text{-}7|$

GH-13. **Algebra Puzzles** Solve these equations.

a) $\tfrac{x}{2} + 7 = 1$

b) $0.5y + 7 = 1$

c) $7 + \tfrac{1}{2}x = 1$

d) What did you notice about parts (a), (b), and (c) in addition to the fact that they have the same answer?

GH-14. Now that we have started a new chapter, it is time for you to organize your binder.

a) Put the work from the last chapter in order and keep it in a separate folder.

b) When this is completed, write "I have organized my binder."

GH-15. Follow your teacher's directions for practicing mental math. Write the steps for one of the methods for solving the problem that was different from yours.

GH-16. We have added fractions using both pictures and paper fraction bars. We have found the least common denominator using ratio tables. We have also found equivalent fractions using the Identity Property of Multiplication (Giant **1**). Today we will use all of these methods. Study the example shown below and use it to help you complete parts (a) through (e) on the resource page that your teacher will give you.

| Question | Picture | Common Denominator Ratio Table | Giant 1 (to get common denominator) |
|---|---|---|---|
| Example: $\frac{2}{3} + \frac{1}{4}$ | thirds $\frac{2}{3}$ + fourths $\frac{1}{4}$ | Compare the common multiples within this ratio table. <br> 3 rds \| 6 \| 9 \| 12 \| 15 <br> 4 ths \| 8 \| 12 \| 16 \| 20 | $\frac{2}{3} \cdot \frac{4}{4} = \frac{8}{12}$ <br> $+ \frac{1}{4} \cdot \frac{3}{3} = \frac{3}{12}$ <br> $\frac{11}{12}$ |

a)  $\frac{1}{5} + \frac{1}{2}$

b)  $\frac{3}{4} + \frac{1}{5}$

c)  $\frac{1}{3} + \frac{1}{4}$

d)  $\frac{1}{2} - \frac{2}{5}$

e)  $\frac{2}{3} - \frac{2}{5}$

GH-17. You have added and subtracted fractions using fraction bars, pictures of rectangles, ratio tables, and the Giant **1**. Which method do you prefer and why?

GH-18. Use the method for adding and subtracting fractions that you prefer to solve these fraction problems. Remember to find common denominators and show all your work.

a)  $\frac{5}{6} - \frac{1}{3}$

b)  $\frac{7}{12} + \frac{1}{4}$

c)  $\frac{7}{4} - \frac{3}{8}$

d)  $\frac{1}{2} + \frac{2}{9}$

e)  $\frac{11}{12} - \frac{1}{6}$

f)  $\frac{7}{8} - \frac{2}{5}$

## ADDING AND SUBTRACTING FRACTIONS

To add or subtract two fractions, the fractions must have the same denominator. One way to convert two fractions with different denominators into fractions with the same denominator is to use the Giant **1**. Below are examples of adding and subtracting two fractions with different denominators. In general,

$$\frac{a}{b} + \frac{c}{d} = \frac{a}{b} \cdot \boxed{\frac{d}{d}} + \frac{c}{d} \cdot \boxed{\frac{b}{b}} = \frac{ad}{bd} + \frac{bc}{bd} = \frac{ad + bc}{bd}$$

### Addition Example

$$\frac{1}{5} + \frac{1}{3} = \frac{1}{5} \cdot \boxed{\frac{3}{3}} + \frac{1}{3} \cdot \boxed{\frac{5}{5}} = \frac{3}{15} + \frac{5}{15} = \frac{8}{15}$$

### Subtraction Example

$$\frac{5}{6} - \frac{1}{4} = \frac{5}{6} \cdot \boxed{\frac{2}{2}} - \frac{1}{4} \cdot \boxed{\frac{3}{3}} = \frac{10}{12} - \frac{3}{12} = \frac{7}{12}$$

Answer the questions below in your Tool Kit to the right of the double-lined box.

a)   What common denominator is needed to compute $\frac{1}{8} + \frac{2}{3}$ ?

b)   Compute $\frac{1}{8} + \frac{2}{3}$ using the Giant **1**. Highlight the Giant **1**s used.

c)   Copy the rectangle model for adding fractions shown in problem GH-16.

---

From this point on, you may use any method <u>except</u> a calculator to solve the fraction problems.

---

GH-20.   Marianne brought $\frac{7}{8}$ pound of candy to school. By lunch she had shared $\frac{1}{3}$ pound of the candy with her friends.

a)   How much candy does she have left by lunch time?

b)   Later in the day, she shares more candy and has $\frac{1}{24}$ pound remaining. How much did she share after lunch?

GH-21. Some players on the basketball team ordered three pizzas for their pizza party. Susie ate $\frac{5}{8}$ of a pizza; Dorothea and Johanna each ate $\frac{3}{8}$ of a pizza; Beth ate $\frac{1}{2}$ of a pizza; Aly ate $\frac{1}{4}$ of a pizza; and Kylee ate $\frac{3}{4}$ of a pizza.

a) How much pizza was eaten altogether?

b) Is there any pizza remaining? If so, how much?

GH-22. Solve these fraction problems. You may want to practice using the Identity Property of Multiplication (Giant **1**).

a) $\frac{1}{5} + \frac{2}{3}$

b) $\frac{3}{4} - \frac{1}{5}$

c) $\frac{5}{6} + \frac{1}{3}$

GH-23. At a recent home game, members of a basketball team gave prizes to their fans. One-third of the fans received pins, $\frac{1}{4}$ received caps, $\frac{1}{6}$ received bats, and $\frac{1}{6}$ received team jerseys. No fan received more than one prize.

a) What fraction of the fans went home with a prize?

b) What fraction of the fans did not go home with a prize?

c) If there were 13,200 fans in attendance, how many fans did not get a prize?

d) How many prizes were given away?

GH-24. Solve each problem using the correct order of operations.

a) $-72 \div (-9) + (-9)$

b) $-72 \div (-9 + (-9))$

c) $-72 \div (-9) - (-9)$

d) $-80 \div 20 - 15 \cdot (-5)$

e) $-80 \div (20 - 15) \cdot (-5)$

f) $-80 \div (20 - 15 \cdot (-5))$

GH-25.  Find the area of each parallelogram.

a)

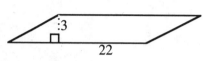

b)

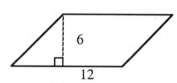

GH-26.  A common way to represent division is by writing a fraction. For example, $3 \div 5 = \frac{3}{5}$.
Write each of the following division problems as a fraction. Simplify each fraction if
possible.

a)  $2 \div 3$

b)  $2 \div 4$

c)  $6 \div 9$

d)  $6 \div 3$

e)  $12 \div 9$

f)  $8 \div 4$

GH-27.  Terrence is cutting ceramic tiles for the
Garcias' new house. His tile cutter can cut
25.8 inches in 1.5 minutes. How many inches
of tile can he cut in the next hour?

GH-28. Today you will make a circle tool called a "circle slider." You and your partner will need two different colors of card stock, a resource page, and scissors. Here are the steps to follow:

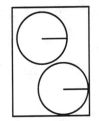

a)   Cut out two circles by cutting carefully along the **circumference**.

b)   After you and your partner have cut out all four circles, cut carefully along the **radius** of each circle to its center.

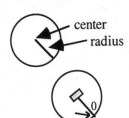

c)   Trade one circle with your partner so that each of you have two different colored circles. Put a piece of clear tape across the **center** of each circle so that the **radius** does not tear any further. Put an arrow below the radius on one circle. Put a zero above the radius on the same circle.

d)   Place the circle with the arrow on top of the second circle and align the cut radii. Slide the flap with the arrow behind the flap with the zero. Rotate the top circle counter-clockwise so the two circles interlock.

You now have a circle slider that can show a variety of circle graphs. You will use it for each of the next several lessons.

GH-29. As your teacher asks you questions similar to the ones below, show the answers on your circle slider. We will refer to the two circles as "light" and "dark."

a)   Move your slider to show $\frac{1}{2}$ light.

b)   Move your slider to show $\frac{1}{4}$ light.

c)   Show $\frac{3}{4}$ light.        d)   Show $\frac{1}{8}$ light.

e)   Show $\frac{3}{8}$ light.        f)   Put away your slides. We will use them again.

GH-30.   You have been using the Giant **1** to add and subtract fractions. Now you will use it with mixed numbers.

When Davis's teacher, Mrs. Olson, gave him some mixed numbers to add, he thought, "All I have to do is add the whole numbers and then add the fractions."

Davis was asked to add $2\frac{1}{6}$ to $3\frac{1}{3}$. He changed the fraction part of each mixed number to the common denominator using the Giant **1**.

$$2\frac{1}{6} = 2 + \frac{1}{6} = 2 + \frac{1}{6} \cdot \boxed{\frac{1}{1}} = 2\frac{1}{6}$$

$$+ \ 3\frac{1}{3} = 3 + \frac{1}{3} = 3 + \frac{1}{3} \cdot \boxed{\frac{2}{2}} = +3\frac{2}{6}$$

As you can see, he added the whole numbers, $2 + 3 = 5$, and then added the fractions, $\frac{1}{6} + \frac{2}{6} = \frac{3}{6}$. He simplified $\frac{3}{6}$ to $\frac{1}{2}$. His final answer is $5\frac{1}{2}$.

$$5\frac{1}{2}$$

Use Davis' method to add the mixed numbers below.

a)  $5\frac{1}{2} + 4\frac{1}{3}$     b)  $4\frac{2}{3} + 3\frac{1}{4}$     c)  $4\frac{1}{3} + 3\frac{1}{5}$     d)  $3\frac{3}{4} + 5\frac{1}{8}$

GH-31.   When Davis saw a subtraction problem, he remembered that he had trouble with this concept last year, especially when he had to borrow. He wondered if there was another way to do it. His partner, Kaylah, reminded him that they had been changing mixed numbers to fractions. She said, "If we change the mixed numbers to fractions we will not need to borrow."

They tried it with the problem at right.

$$2\frac{1}{2} - 1\frac{3}{4}$$

*Davis:*   First I change the mixed numbers to fractions.

$$2\frac{1}{2} = \frac{5}{2}$$

$$-1\frac{3}{4} = -\frac{7}{4}$$

*Kaylah:*   Oh! Then you can change the fractions so they have a common denominator— fourths.

$$\frac{5}{2} \cdot \boxed{\frac{2}{2}} = \frac{10}{4}$$

$$-\frac{7}{4} = -\frac{7}{4}$$

*Davis:*   Now, we can subtract 7 from 10 and get our answer.

$$\frac{3}{4}$$

**>>Problem continues on the next page.>>**

*Kaylah:* So for each subtraction problem we can change the mixed numbers to fractions greater than one, find common denominators, and then subtract.

Try Davis and Kaylah's method for these problems.

a) $3\frac{1}{3} - 2\frac{1}{2}$

b) $2\frac{1}{4} - 1\frac{1}{3}$

c) $3\frac{1}{3} - 2\frac{2}{5}$

d) $3 - 1\frac{3}{4}$

GH-32. Here is a graphical look at proportions and percents. Copy and complete the table.

| Picture | Problem in Words / Proportion | Answer |
|---|---|---|
| 32 ⌐ 100%  20 ⌐ n  0 └ 0% | What percent of 32 is 20? $\frac{n}{100\%} = \frac{20}{32\%}$  $32 \cdot n = 100 \cdot 20$  $32n = 625 \cdot 32$ | $62.50\%$ |
| Sketch and shade the picture. Fill in the missing parts.  6 ⌐ 100%  0 └ 0% | What percent of 6 is 5.58? $\frac{n}{100} = \frac{5.58}{6}$  $n \cdot 6 = 100 \cdot 5.58$  $\frac{n6}{6} = \frac{558}{6}$  $n = 93\%$ | $93\%$ |

GH-33.

Answer the questions below in your Tool Kit to the right of the double-lined box.

a)  Highlight the method you prefer.

b)  Use the method you prefer to compute $2\frac{5}{8} + 3\frac{1}{6}$. Check that your work is correct with your partner or team members.

GH-34.  Add or subtract to simplify the following pairs of fractions.

a)  $7\frac{1}{3} + 4\frac{1}{2}$

b)  $7 - 3\frac{2}{3}$

c)  $6\frac{2}{3} + 2\frac{1}{4}$

d)  $-8\frac{1}{5} + 4\frac{1}{2}$

GH-35.  Solve the following problems using the correct order of operations.

a)  $16 + 2 \cdot 3 - 5 \cdot 2$

b)  $(-79 + 2) \div 11 - 5 - 2$

c)  $24 \div 2 + 6 \cdot 3 - (2 + 5) \cdot 2$

d)  $(3 - 5) \cdot (1 - 2) - (3 - 2) \cdot (5 + 1)$

GH-36.    Find the area of each trapezoid.  Look back in your Tool Kit for information about trapezoids if needed.

a)

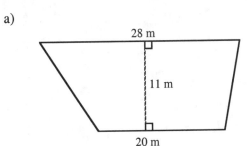

b)

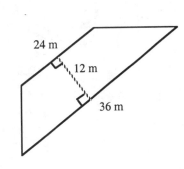

GH-37.    Set up and solve the following problems using proportions.  Be sure to label the units.

a)    Mrs. Garcia can make four quilts in 90 days.  Working at the same rate, how many days will it take her to make six quilts?

b)    It will take the carpenters two days to frame three rooms in the Garcias' house.  Working at the same rate, how long will it take them to frame the other seven rooms?

c)    Davis can do 15 math problems in 32 minutes.  Working at the same rate, how long will it take him to finish the assignment of 50 problems?

d)    It took Kaylah 36 minutes to do 15 problems.  Working at the same rate, how long will it take her to finish the assignment of 50 problems?

GH-38.    Sometimes division problems do not have whole number answers.  For example, $7 \div 2$.

a)    $7 \div 2$ means, "How many ___ are in ___ ?"

b)    How many whole sets of two are in seven?

c)    What fraction of a set of two remains?

d)    Explain why the answer to $7 \div 2 = 3\frac{1}{2}$ makes sense.

e)    Write $7 \div 2$ as a fraction and evaluate that fraction.  What answer do you get?

GH-39.    **Algebra Puzzles**  Solve these equations.

a)    $\frac{w}{4} - 6 = -3$          b)    $0.25x - 6 = -3$          c)    $\frac{1}{4}y - 6 = -3$

d)    Why are the answers to (a), (b), and (c) the same?


GH-40.    Take out your circle slider.  As your teacher asks you questions similar to the ones below, show the answers on your slider.

a)    Move your slider counter-clockwise so that it shows $\frac{1}{2}$ light. The cut edge of the light circle is labeled with 0, which we will use as a reference line.  On the light circle of your slider, draw a radius and label it with the fraction $\frac{1}{2}$ .

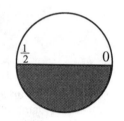

b)    Move your slider counter-clockwise so that it  shows $\frac{1}{4}$ light. Draw and label a radius to mark $\frac{1}{4}$ on your slider.

c)    Move your slider counter-clockwise so that it shows $\frac{3}{4}$ light.  Draw and label a radius for this fraction.

d)    Draw and label a radius for the fraction $\frac{1}{8}$ light.

e)    Find all of the other eighths on your light slider circle.  Draw each radius and label the corresponding fraction.  If you are not sure where they are, check with your partner.

f)    List two equivalent fractions for $\frac{1}{2}$ .

g)    Put away your sliders.  We will use them again.


GH-41.    Solve the following problems without paper or pencil.

a)    What is one-eighth of sixteen?

b)    What is one-eighth of twenty-four?

c)    What is three-eighths of forty?

GH-42.    Obtain the unit rectangle resource page from your teacher or draw eight rectangles on a full sheet of paper.

Garden Road Middle School is planning a field trip for the girls to attend a conference about careers in mathematics. If half of the students are girls and three-fourths of them bring in permission slips to attend the field trip, what fraction of students in the school will be able to go on the field trip?

a)    The entire school's enrollment can be represented with an unshaded unit rectangle. Half of the school is girls. Divide your rectangle into two equal pieces. Shade and label one of the halves to show half the school is girls.

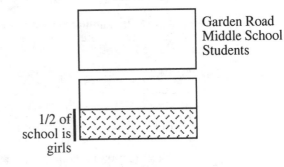

Garden Road Middle School Students

1/2 of school is girls

b)    Label the other half.

1/2 of school is boys

c)    Three-fourths of the girls brought back their permission slips to go to the conference. Use vertical lines to cut the original (large) rectangle in fourths, then darkly shade $\frac{3}{4}$ of the girls' section.

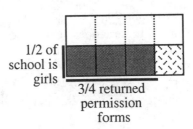

1/2 of school is girls

3/4 returned permission forms

The darkly shaded region shows "$\frac{3}{4}$ of $\frac{1}{2}$ of the school."

d)    What fraction of the whole school is "$\frac{3}{4}$ of $\frac{1}{2}$"?

GH-43. Howie has $\frac{5}{8}$ of a pizza left over from last night's dinner. He loves pizza and eats half of the remaining $\frac{5}{8}$ pizza the next day for breakfast. Draw a rectangle or use your unit rectangle resource page and follow the steps below to determine how much of the original pizza Howie ate for breakfast.

   a)  We want to know how much is $\frac{1}{2}$ of $\frac{5}{8}$. Since Howie ate $\frac{1}{2}$ of $\frac{5}{8}$, we draw the $\frac{5}{8}$ first. In a unit rectangle, draw $\frac{5}{8}$ on your resource page using vertical lines and shade it lightly. Label it "$\frac{5}{8}$ leftover pizza."

   b)  Using a horizontal line, divide the unit rectangle in half.

   c)  Darkly shade $\frac{1}{2}$ of $\frac{5}{8}$ and label it, "Howie eats $\frac{1}{2}$."

   d)  Write an equation in the form $\frac{1}{2}$ of $\frac{5}{8}$ = ___ .

GH-44. Joe Dominguez has decided to plant a rectangular flower garden. Joe loves dark carnations. He wants one-half of the garden to be planted with carnations. One-third of the carnations must be dark.

   a)  On a unit rectangle, label and shade the fraction of the garden which must be carnations.

   b)  Now label and shade the fraction of the carnations which must be dark.

   c)  Complete this statement with fractions:
       "_____ of _____ of the garden is dark carnations."

   d)  What fraction of the whole garden must be dark carnations?

   e)  What fraction of the garden is not dark carnations?                —

GH-45. Frieda Friendly works for a local car dealership. She noticed that $\frac{3}{4}$ of the cars are sedans and that half of them are white. What fraction of the dealership's cars are white sedans?

   a)  Use a unit rectangle to represent this situation. Label the parts carefully.

   b)  Write an equation or a sentence that describes the situation, and answer the question.

GH-46.　Write a fraction sentence for each drawing.

Example:

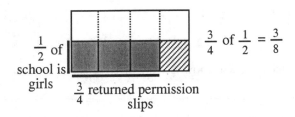

$\frac{1}{2}$ of school is girls

$\frac{3}{4}$ returned permission slips

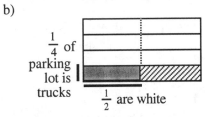

$\frac{3}{4}$ of $\frac{1}{2}$ = $\frac{3}{8}$

a)

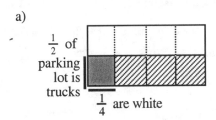

$\frac{1}{2}$ of parking lot is trucks

$\frac{1}{4}$ are white

b)

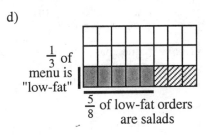

$\frac{1}{4}$ of parking lot is trucks

$\frac{1}{2}$ are white

c)

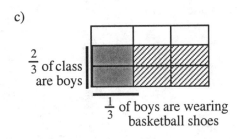

$\frac{2}{3}$ of class are boys

$\frac{1}{3}$ of boys are wearing basketball shoes

d)

$\frac{1}{3}$ of menu is "low-fat"

$\frac{5}{8}$ of low-fat orders are salads

GH-47.    In parts (a) and (b) of the preceding problem, the rectangular models for $\frac{1}{2}$ of $\frac{1}{4}$ and $\frac{1}{4}$ of $\frac{1}{2}$ look different, but the answers are the same. Below is an example of how to multiply $\frac{2}{3} \cdot \frac{2}{5}$ by shading a rectangle. Read the steps and then draw a similar sequence of rectangles to show $\frac{2}{5} \cdot \frac{2}{3}$. Are the answers the same? Why or why not?

---

### MULTIPLYING FRACTIONS BY SHADING A RECTANGLE

One way to model multiplying fractions is to shade a unit rectangle. Here is an example of shading a unit rectangle to represent $\frac{2}{3}$ of $\frac{2}{5}$ or, written as multiplication, $\frac{2}{3} \cdot \frac{2}{5}$.

Step 1    Divide a rectangle into five sections ("fifths")—the denominator of the second fraction. (Notice that the second number has been drawn first.)

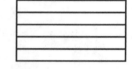

Step 2    Shade horizontal sections to represent how many fifths there are—the numerator of the second fraction.

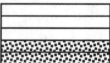

Step 3    Divide the rectangle vertically using the denominator of the other factor ("thirds").

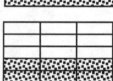

Step 4    Use a darker shading to show how many thirds there are. For this example, shade two-thirds of the two-fifths.

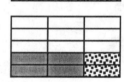

Step 5    The product's numerator is the number of sections that are double-shaded. The product's denominator is the total number of sections in the rectangle. Write an equation to show the product: $\frac{2}{3} \cdot \frac{2}{5} = \frac{4}{15}$. Simplify or reduce the product when possible.

---

GH-48.    Use the Identity Property of Multiplication (Giant **1**) to add or subtract each pair of fractions.

a)    $\frac{2}{5} + \frac{1}{3}$          b)    $\frac{3}{4} + \frac{1}{3}$          c)    $\frac{3}{5} - \frac{1}{2}$

GH-49.   Find each of the following.

   a)    $|-62| + |-26|$

   b)    $-|-19|$

   c)    $|0.5| - |-1\frac{1}{2}|$

   d)    $|14| + |-15|$


GH-50.   Simplify.

   a)    $-4 + (-8) \cdot (-2) - (-7)$

   b)    $\dfrac{-3 + 8(-2)}{19} \div \dfrac{-4}{-2(-2)}$

   c)    $\dfrac{10 \div (-2 \cdot 2\frac{1}{2})}{-4 \div (-2)}$

   d)    $\dfrac{-7 \cdot 5}{-45 \div 9}$


GH-51.   **Algebra Puzzles**   How are these problems the same?  In what ways are they different?

   a)    $\frac{x}{5} + 18 = 11$

   b)    $0.5y + 2 = 3$

   c)    $0.2x + 18 = 11$

   d)    $\frac{y}{2} + 2 = 3$


GH-52.   Marvin has a bag of 20 marbles.  Five marbles are light, six are dark, four are yellow, two are blue, and three are orange.  If he takes out one marble without looking, what is the probability that he pulls out a yellow marble?


GH-53.   Solve the following percentage questions using proportions.

   a)    The original price of a snowboard is $420.  What is the sale price after a 20% discount?

   b)    You pay $0.45 for a candy bar that normally costs $0.60. What percentage is the discount?

   c)    Roller blades were being discontinued at the local sporting goods store.  If Steve bought a pair for $60 after a 40% discount, what was the original price? (Suggestion: Think about the percent of the original price Steve paid.)

GH-54.    Mrs. Olson had to find the class average for the last math test. She also needed to give the school principal information about how well the class was doing. The test scores were 89, 92, 45, 90, 65, 54, 68, 75, 77, 86, 85, 72, 38, 85, 91, 85, 10, 70, 65, and 73.

a)    Make a stem-and-leaf plot of the test scores.

b)    Find the mean, median, and mode of the scores.

c)    Which measure do you think most fairly represents how well the class is doing?


GH-55.    Take out your circle sliders. As your teacher asks you questions similar to the ones below, show the answers on your sliders.

a)    Move your slider to show 50%. Mark that percent on your light slider. What fraction does it match?

b)    Show 75% on your slider. Label that percent.

c)    Show 25%. Label that percent.

d)    Show and label 12.5%.

e)    Mark each of the eighths on your slider with its corresponding percent.

f)    List the percentages equal to $\frac{1}{8}$, $\frac{3}{8}$, $\frac{5}{8}$, and $\frac{7}{8}$ on your paper next to problem GH-55. Write each one as an equation.

g)    Put your sliders away. We will use them again.

GH-56. While working in class Stephanie had to do the
problem $\frac{3}{5} \cdot \frac{6}{7}$. She started to draw rectangles to
solve the problem. Stephanie looked over at Audrey's
work and saw that Audrey was way ahead of her.
"How did you get so far ahead of me? Why aren't
you drawing rectangles for these problems?"

Audrey said, "I found a shortcut. Didn't you notice
that when we drew the rectangles, we got the same thing
as if we had multiplied the numerators and then
multiplied the denominators? Look at problem GH-47.
All we had to do was say, 'Two times two is four and
three times five is fifteen.' You get the same answer,
four-fifteenths, without the drawing. So when I saw these problems, I decided I wasn't
going to draw the rectangles with all those little pieces. I just said $3 \cdot 6 = 18$ and
$5 \cdot 7 = 35$ and got $\frac{18}{35}$. It was a lot faster."

a)   Check Audrey's method using a rectangle model.

b)   What information does multiplying $5 \cdot 7$ tell you about the model?

c)   What information does multiplying $3 \cdot 6$ tell you about the model?


GH-57. Use Audrey's method to multiply each of the following pairs of fractions.

a)   $\frac{7}{8} \cdot \frac{5}{6}$

b)   $\frac{2}{13} \cdot \frac{4}{5}$

c)   $\frac{6}{7} \cdot \frac{6}{7}$

d)   $\frac{4}{7} \cdot \frac{3}{8}$

e)   $\frac{6}{11} \cdot \frac{1}{2}$

f)   $\frac{8}{3} \cdot \frac{9}{14}$

GH-58.

```
┌──────────────────────────────────────────────────────────────┐
│                   MULTIPLYING TWO FRACTIONS                    │
│                                                                │
│  Multiplying two fractions gives you a new fraction (which     │
│  you might be able to simplify to a whole number). The         │
│  numerator of the new fraction is the product of the two       │
│  original numerators. The denominator is the product of the    │
│  two original denominators                                     │
└──────────────────────────────────────────────────────────────┘
```

For example:                          In general:

$$\frac{2}{3} \cdot \frac{2}{7} = \frac{2 \cdot 2}{3 \cdot 7} = \frac{4}{21} \qquad\qquad \frac{a}{b} \cdot \frac{c}{d} = \frac{ac}{bd}$$

Sometimes you will need to simplify the product.

$$\frac{2}{3} \cdot \frac{3}{5} = \frac{2 \cdot 3}{3 \cdot 5} = \frac{6}{15} = \left(\frac{2}{5} \cdot \frac{3}{3}\right) = \frac{2}{5}$$

Sometimes it is easier to simplify the fractions before multiplying.

$$\left(\frac{8}{12}\right)\left(\frac{6}{15}\right) = \left(\frac{2}{3} \cdot \frac{4}{4}\right)\left(\frac{2}{5} \cdot \frac{3}{3}\right) = \left(\frac{2}{3}\right)\left(\frac{2}{5}\right) = \frac{4}{15}$$

Answer the following questions in your Tool Kit to the right of the double-lined box.

a)     Highlight the Giant **1**s that you see in the examples above.

b)     Explain how the Giant **1** is used to simplify fractions.

GH-59.     Use a generic rectangle to find the product $43 \cdot 32$.

GH-60.     Ronna is making a small flower bed that is $1\frac{1}{2}$ feet by $1\frac{1}{2}$ feet. She needs to find the area so she can add the correct amount of fertilizer to the soil.

Draw the rectangle shown below on your paper. Complete steps (a) through (d).

a)     Label the top and side 1 foot and $\frac{1}{2}$ foot as shown.

b)     Write the area in each of the four parts of the drawing and find the total area.

c)     Write an equation that represents the sum of the four areas.

d)     Compare your answer and equation to those of your partner or teammates. Did you get the same answer? Did you get the same equations?

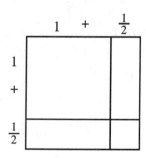

GH-61.    Using the process shown in the previous problem, find the area
of Ronna's flower bed if the dimensions are $2\frac{1}{2}$ feet by $1\frac{1}{2}$ feet.
Clearly label all dimensions.

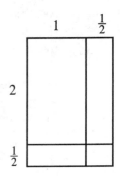

GH-62.

## MULTIPLYING MIXED NUMBERS
### (based on the Distributive Property)

To multiply mixed numbers, you may use a generic rectangle (based on the
Distributive Property).

Example:

$$2\frac{1}{2} \cdot 1\frac{1}{4} = (2 + \frac{1}{2}) \cdot (1 + \frac{1}{4})$$

$$= 2(1) + 2(\frac{1}{4}) + \frac{1}{2}(1) + \frac{1}{2}(\frac{1}{4})$$

$$= 2 + \frac{2}{4} + \frac{1}{2} + \frac{1}{8}$$

$$= 2 + \frac{1}{2} + \frac{1}{2} + \frac{1}{8}$$

$$= 2 + 1 + \frac{1}{8}$$

$$= 3\frac{1}{8}$$

Put one of the solved problems from below in your Tool Kit to the right of the double-
lined box. Check with your partner or team that your work is correct.

GH-63.    Given the dimensions below, use drawings to find the area of the rectangles. Make sure
you clearly label each rectangle.

a)    $1\frac{1}{3} \cdot 1\frac{1}{2}$                         b)    $3\frac{1}{3} \cdot 2\frac{1}{2}$

c)    $2\frac{1}{2} \cdot 2\frac{1}{2}$                         d)    $2\frac{1}{2} \cdot 1\frac{1}{4}$

GH-64.   As Jonique was working in class, she had to do the problem $2\frac{1}{2} \cdot 3\frac{1}{4}$. She figured out a shortcut for multiplying mixed numbers. "I know how to change mixed numbers into fractions. After I do that, I can just multiply the fractions."

Look at Jonique's work:   $2\frac{1}{2} \cdot 3\frac{1}{4} = \frac{5}{2} \cdot \frac{13}{4} = \frac{65}{8} = 8\frac{1}{8}$

Try Jonique's shortcut on the following problems. Show each step like she did.

a)   $3\frac{1}{2} \cdot 2\frac{1}{4}$          b)   $1\frac{1}{3} \cdot 2\frac{1}{2}$          c)   $1\frac{1}{3} \cdot 3\frac{1}{3}$

d)   Compare part (a) with the Tool Kit example in problem GH-62. Which method do you prefer? Why?

GH-65.

---

**MULTIPLYING MIXED NUMBERS
USING FRACTIONS GREATER THAN ONE**

To multiply mixed numbers, first change them to fractions greater than one. Then multiply.

Example:   $2\frac{1}{2} \cdot 1\frac{1}{4} = \frac{5}{2} \cdot \frac{5}{4} = \frac{25}{8} = 3\frac{1}{8}$

---

GH-66.   Here is a fast mental math technique to solve $\frac{5}{6} \cdot 24$. Remember that $\frac{5}{6} = 5 \cdot \frac{1}{6}$.

a)   What is ONE-sixth of 24?

b)   What is five times that quantity?

c)   What is $\frac{5}{6} \cdot 24$?

GH-67.   Use the above method to mentally calculate each product. Write an equation for each problem.

a)   $\frac{3}{4} \cdot 24$          b)   $\frac{3}{8} \cdot 32$          c)   $\frac{4}{7} \cdot 35$

GH-68.    While going on a field trip, a busload of 54
students will have to be split up into three groups.
Two-thirds will go to lunch first and one-third
will go visit the exhibits.  How many will go to
lunch first?  Write an equation to represent the
problem.

GH-69.    At your first job you may be amazed to learn that one-fourth of your paycheck will go to
pay taxes. Suppose the amounts listed in parts (a) through (c) are the earnings for three
employees.  Determine how much of each paycheck will go to pay taxes.

a)    $84              b)    $128              c)    $210

GH-70.    Find the area of each triangle below.

a)                                          b)

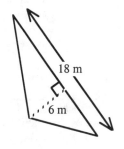

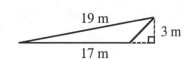

c)                                          d)

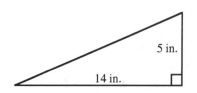

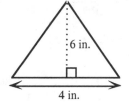

GH-71.    Simplify each expression.

a)    $(4 + 8) \div 12 + 23$              b)    $3 \cdot (8 - 5) + 6 + 2 \cdot 7$

c)    $4 \cdot (9 + 6) + \frac{3}{4} \cdot 8$              d)    $49 \div 7 \cdot 5 + 4 \cdot (3 + 2)$

GH-72.    Take out your circle sliders. As your teacher asks you questions similar to the ones below, show the answers on your sliders.

   a)   Move your slider so that it shows the fraction $\frac{1}{3}$ light. Show and label the fraction and percent on your slider.

   b)   Show and label $\frac{2}{3}$ on your slider as a fraction and a percent.

   c)   One person likes root beer and two people like cola. Show the circle graph of the fraction who like cola.

   d)   Move your slider so that it shows $\frac{5}{8}$. Did you move the slider very far?

   e)   Move your slider so that it shows that 1 out of 5 dentists recommend Crystal Fresh toothpaste. Did you move the slider very far?

   f)   Write an equivalent fraction and percentage next to problem GH-72 on your paper. Put your sliders away. We will use them again.

GH-73.    Jo wrote her name using masking tape that is $\frac{3}{4}$ inch wide. Calculate lengths a, b, and c in inches.

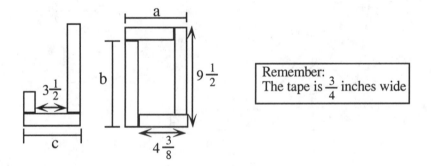

Remember:
The tape is $\frac{3}{4}$ inches wide

GH-74.    In carpentry, the piece of lumber called a "two-by-four" is NOT actually 2 inches by 4 inches. The wood is "rough cut" to 2 inches by 4 inches but then each of the four faces (sides) of the wood is "milled" (sanded) down by $\frac{1}{4}$ inch. What are the finished dimensions of a two-by-four?

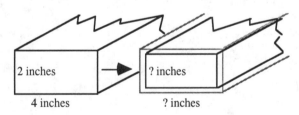

**GH-75.** Sandy is a contractor working for the Garcias. She knows that a two-by-four is actually $1\frac{1}{2}$ x $3\frac{1}{2}$ inches. She needs to cut a $1\frac{1}{2}$ x $3\frac{1}{2}$-inch piece of lumber in half in both directions. What will be the dimensions of each of the four pieces? You can assume the width of her saw blade is zero (that is, ignore the small loss of wood from the cut). You do not need to worry about how long the lumber is.

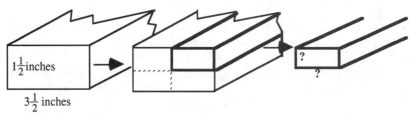

**GH-76.** Sandy needs to cut a $3\frac{1}{2}$ x $5\frac{1}{2}$-inch piece of lumber (called a four-by-six) in half along the short side and in thirds along the long side. What will be the dimensions of each of the six pieces?

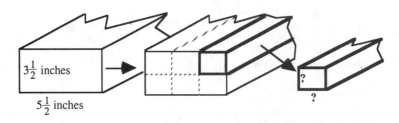

**GH-77.**

Sandy needs to frame a doorway so that the finished opening is $32\frac{1}{8}$ x $80\frac{1}{4}$ inches. Study the picture below and decide what lengths of two-by-fours she should cut. Remember that a two-by-four is actually $1\frac{1}{2}$ x $3\frac{1}{2}$ inches.

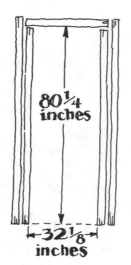

GH-78. All of Sandy's two-by-fours start as boards 96 inches long.

    a) What length would remain if she cut off $81\frac{3}{4}$ inches?

    b) What length would remain if she cut off two pieces, each $24\frac{3}{8}$ inches?

    c) What length would remain if she cut off three pieces, each $16\frac{7}{8}$ inches?

GH-79. Multiply. Be sure to simplify when possible.

    a) $\frac{5}{8} \cdot \frac{4}{5}$          b) $\frac{6}{7} \cdot \frac{7}{10}$          c) $\frac{3}{4} \cdot \frac{16}{27}$

GH-80. For parts (a) and (b), find the products using a rectangle. For parts (c) and (d), change to fractions and multiply.

    a) $2\frac{1}{4} \cdot 1\frac{1}{4}$                b) $3\frac{1}{3} \cdot 3\frac{1}{2}$

    c) $2\frac{1}{2} \cdot 2\frac{1}{4}$                d) $1\frac{1}{8} \cdot \frac{3}{8}$

    e) Which method do you prefer and why?

GH-81. Complete the following Diamond Problems.

Product

Sum

a)

b)

c)

d)

GH-82. Simplify each pair of fractions.

    a) $3\frac{3}{4} \cdot 1\frac{1}{5}$                b) $3\frac{3}{4} - 1\frac{1}{5}$

    c) $2\frac{1}{4} + 4\frac{1}{3}$                d) $\frac{7}{3} + \frac{3}{5}$

GH-83.    Mrs. Poppington was looking at her roll book
          and said, "Five-eighths of the students in my
          fourth-period class are boys."  She has 32
          students on the list.

          a)    How many boys are in the class?

          b)    How many girls are in the class?

GH-84.    **Algebra Puzzles**   Solve these equations.  These may appear to be more difficult than
          they are.

          a)    $2w - 2\frac{1}{3} = 1\frac{2}{3}$              b)    $5\frac{1}{8} - 2x = -4\frac{7}{8}$

GH-85.    Take out your circle sliders.  As your teacher asks you questions similar to the ones
          below, show the answers on your sliders.

          a)    Move your slider so that it shows 500 thousandths.  Label this line as a decimal.
                Was this a number you labeled earlier?

          b)    Move your slider so that it shows 250 thousandths.  Label this line as a decimal.
                What fraction is this number?  What percent is this?

          c)    Find 125 thousandths.  Mark this line as a decimal.  To what fraction does it
                correspond?  What percent?

          d)    Mark the other eighths with their matching decimals.  Discuss this with your
                partner.

          e)    Show 875 thousandths on the light circle.

          f)    Show one-third.  Mark it with both the percent and the decimal.

          g)    Mark two-thirds in the same manner.

          h)    Write the fraction, decimal, and percent equivalents for $\frac{1}{3}$ on your paper next to
                problem GH-85.

          i)    Put your sliders away in your binder.

GH-86.    Solve these fraction division problems.

a)    How many one-thirds are in 1 whole?  That is, what is $1 \div \frac{1}{3}$?

b)    How many one-thirds are in 3?  That is, what is $3 \div \frac{1}{3}$?

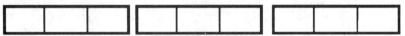

c)    How many one-fourths are in 5?  That is, what is $5 \div \frac{1}{4}$?

d)    How many one-sixths are in 3?  That is, what is $3 \div \frac{1}{6}$?

e)    How many one-fifths are in 6?  That is, what is $6 \div \frac{1}{5}$?

f)    How many one-sevenths are in 3?  That is, what is $3 \div \frac{1}{7}$?

GH-87.    Write a sentence that tells the meaning of the following expressions.  Then do the division.

Example:  $2 \div \frac{1}{3}$  means, "How many one-thirds are in 2?" or  $2 \div \frac{1}{3} = 6$.

a)    $2 \div \frac{1}{4}$          b)    $5 \div \frac{1}{2}$          c)    $3 \div \frac{1}{5}$

GH-88.    Sometimes division problems do not have whole-number answers but have an answer which is a fraction or a mixed number.  An example of such a problem is  $10 \div 4$.

a)    How many <u>whole</u> sets of four are in ten?

b)    What fraction of the next set of 4 is used?

c)    Explain why the answer to  $10 \div 4 = 2\frac{1}{2}$  makes sense.

GH-89.    Let's look at another division problem with a fractional answer.

   a)   Write a sentence that asks the same question as "$\frac{3}{4} \div \frac{1}{2} = ?$"
        Refer to problem GH-87 if you need help.

   b)   How many <u>complete</u> $\frac{1}{2}$ s are shaded in the $\frac{3}{4}$ ?

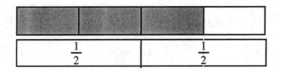

   c)   What fraction of another $\frac{1}{2}$ is also shaded?

   d)   Explain why the answer to $\frac{3}{4} \div \frac{1}{2} = 1\frac{1}{2}$ makes sense.


GH-90.    Complete steps (a) through (e) using $8 \div 3$.

   a)   $8 \div 3$ means, "_____."    b)   How many whole sets of 3 are in 8?

   c)   What fraction of 3 remains?           d)   Explain why $8 \div 3 = 2\frac{2}{3}$ makes sense.

   e)   Write $8 \div 3$ as a fraction and evaluate the fraction.


GH-91.    Complete the resource page provided by your teacher for the following six problems. An example is given here.

| Problem | Problem in Words | Fraction Bar Picture | Answer |
|---|---|---|---|
| Example: $1\frac{2}{3} \div \frac{1}{6}$ | How many $\frac{1}{6}$ s are in $1\frac{2}{3}$ ? | 1  2  3  4  5  6   7  8  9  10 | 10 |

   a)   $\frac{3}{2} \div \frac{3}{4}$         b)   $1\frac{1}{8} \div \frac{1}{4}$        c)   $\frac{1}{2} \div \frac{1}{3}$

   d)   $1\frac{3}{4} \div \frac{1}{2}$         e)   $1\frac{5}{6} \div \frac{1}{3}$        f)   $1\frac{1}{2} \div \frac{1}{3}$

GH-92.   Copy and complete the following equations.

a)   $\frac{1}{7} \cdot \frac{7}{1} = \square$   b)   $\frac{1}{5} \cdot \frac{\square}{\square} = 1$   c)   $\frac{3}{2} \cdot \frac{\square}{\square} = 1$   d)   $\frac{5}{\square} \cdot \frac{2}{\square} = 1$

e)   What do all of the problems above have in common?

GH-93.   There is only one positive number that is equal to its reciprocal. What is it?

(A) 0                     (B) $\frac{1}{2}$                     (C) 1                     (D) 2

GH-94.

**RECIPROCALS**

Two numbers that have a product of 1 are called **reciprocals**.

Examples:

$$\frac{5}{8} \cdot \frac{8}{5} = \frac{40}{40} = 1 \qquad 3\frac{1}{4} \cdot \frac{4}{13} = \frac{13}{4} \cdot \frac{4}{13} = \frac{52}{52} = 1 \qquad 0.25 \cdot 4 = 1.00$$

In general:

$$a \cdot \frac{1}{a} = 1 \text{ and } \frac{a}{b} \cdot \frac{b}{a} = 1 \text{ where } a \text{ and } b \text{ are not 0.}$$

Answer the questions below in your Tool Kit to the right of the double-lined box.

a)   Show the reciprocals of $\frac{1}{5}$, $\frac{2}{3}$, and $\frac{4}{5}$.

b)   Write a sentence to explain in your own words what reciprocals are.

GH-95.   Since $\frac{1}{5}$ and 5 are reciprocals, we know that $\frac{1}{5} \cdot 5 = 1$.

a)   What do you think $\frac{2}{5} \cdot 5$ equals?   b)   Calculate $\frac{3}{7} \cdot 7$.
     Calculate it.

c)   Calculate $\frac{4}{3} \cdot 3$.                 d)   Without calculating, find $\frac{12}{57} \cdot 57$.

GH-96. Justin is a baker. He knows the recipe for two loaves of Ciabatta (Italian Slipper Bread) but he needs the recipe for other quantities. Get a resource page from your teacher to complete the problem or copy and complete the table below.

| Ingredient | 1 Loaf | 2 Loaves | 3 Loaves | 8 Loaves |
|---|---|---|---|---|
| warm milk | | $2\frac{1}{4}$ Tbs. | | |
| active dry yeast | | $\frac{3}{4}$ tsp. | | |
| room-temperature water | | $\frac{2}{3}$ cups | | |
| olive oil | | $1\frac{1}{2}$ Tbs. | | |
| bread flour | | $2\frac{1}{4}$ cups | | |
| salt | | $1\frac{1}{4}$ tsp. | | |

GH-97. If the weather forecaster says that there is a 60% chance of rain today and a 40% chance of rain tomorrow, do you think it means that there is 100% chance of rain in the next two days? Explain why or why not.

GH-98. Here is a graphical look at proportions and percents. Copy and complete the table.

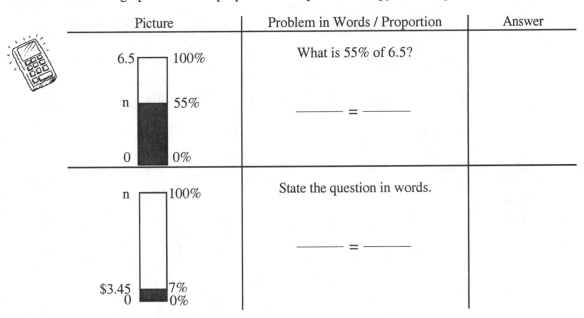

| Picture | Problem in Words / Proportion | Answer |
|---|---|---|
| 6.5 — 100%; n — 55%; 0 — 0% | What is 55% of 6.5? <br><br> ——— = ——— | |
| n — 100%; $3.45 — 7%; 0 — 0% | State the question in words. <br><br> ——— = ——— | |

GH-99.    Follow your teacher's directions for practicing mental math.


GH-100.   Use a ruler to draw a line exactly 4 inches long and then mark every $\frac{1}{2}$ inch.

    a)    How many $\frac{1}{2}$ inches are in 4 inches?

    b)    Use the ruler to mark every $\frac{1}{4}$ inch. How many $\frac{1}{4}$ inches are in 1 inch?

    c)    How many $\frac{1}{4}$ inches are in 2 inches? in 3 inches?

    d)    Mark each $\frac{1}{8}$ inch. How many $\frac{1}{8}$ inches are in 3 inches?


GH-101.   At the school's fall bake sale all of the pies were cut into 6 pieces, so each person who bought a piece bought $\frac{1}{6}$ of a pie. Each slice of pie sold for $1.00. How much money did the school make if all eleven pies were sold?


GH-102.   Answer the questions below.

    a)    How many 5s are in 15?          b)    How many 8s are in 56?

    c)    How would you write each of the questions in parts (a) and (b) as a division problem?


GH-103.   Here is another way to look at some of the problems we did with a ruler.

    a)    How many $\frac{1}{2}$s are in 4?          b)    Write part (a) as a division problem.

    c)    How many $\frac{1}{4}$s are in 3?          d)    Write part (c) as a division problem.

GH-104. Use a ruler to draw a line segment exactly 3 inches long marking every $\frac{1}{4}$ inch. Now mark off $\frac{3}{4}$ inch pieces of this segment.

a)   How many $\frac{3}{4}$ inches are there in 3 inches?

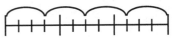

b)   Write part (a) as a division problem.

c)   How many $\frac{3}{4}$ inches are in 1 inch?

d)   Write part (c) as a division problem.

e)   How many $\frac{3}{4}$ inches are there in 2 inches?

f)   Write part (e) as a division problem.

GH-105. Ahmal thought that $5$ inches $\div \frac{3}{4}$ inches was hard to do. He could see and count that there were six $\frac{3}{4}$ inches for the first $4\frac{1}{2}$ inches (count them yourself). What was left was just a part of $\frac{3}{4}$ of an inch.

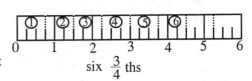

six $\frac{3}{4}$ ths

The piece of a ruler at right shows that this is 2 fourths out of 3 fourths, or just $\frac{2}{3}$.

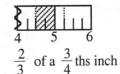

$\frac{2}{3}$ of a $\frac{3}{4}$ ths inch

Ahmal then had an idea for an easier way to find how many $\frac{3}{4}$ ths there were. "Since there are 4 fourths in 1 inch, I can multiply 5 inches by 4 to find out how many $\frac{1}{4}$ ths there are. Then, I can divide that product by 3 to see how many $\frac{3}{4}$ ths there are."

Try Ahmal's idea to calculate $5 \div \frac{3}{4}$. Multiply 5 times 4 and then divide by 3. How many $\frac{3}{4}$ ths are in 5 inches? The ruler should help you check your answer.

GH-106. Try Ahmal's method for the problems below. Use the ruler in the previous problem if you need help visualizing what is being asked.

a)   $4 \div \frac{3}{4}$

b)   $1 \div \frac{3}{4}$

GH-107.   In the meantime, Malik has been thinking about division. He knows that $2 \div 7$ is the same as $\frac{2}{7}$.

Malik:      Since that's true, then I could just say $5 \div \frac{3}{4} = \dfrac{5}{\frac{3}{4}}$.

Cheryl:    That's ugly, Malik. That's a super fraction.

Malik:      Yeah, but then I can use a Giant **1**!

Then Malik writes: $\dfrac{5}{\frac{3}{4}} \cdot \dfrac{4}{4}$.

a)   Complete Malik's problem by multiplying and then simplifying.

b)   Compare Malik's method with Ahmal's. You may want to refer back to GH-106.

GH-108.   Use both Ahmal's and Malik's methods to solve $3 \div \frac{2}{3}$.

GH-109.   Use either Ahmal's OR Malik's method to solve $2 \div \frac{3}{5}$.

GH-110.   Simplify the following expressions.

a)   $-8 + (-8) + (-8) + 24$     b)   $-10 - (-10)$     c)   $36 + (-6) \cdot 5$

d)   $10(2) - (-2)(10)$     e)   $3 + (-2)(3) - 3$     f)   $98 + (-2)(10) - 9(5)$

GH-111.   A family of four will eat 90.3 pounds of fruits and vegetables on board the *Oriana* luxury ocean liner during a two-week cruise.

a)   How many pounds of fruits and vegetables will be purchased and brought aboard if 2736 people will be on the ship?

b)   A ton is 2,000 pounds. Convert your answer from part (a) into tons.

GH-112. Ahmal and Kezer were checking the prices of some stocks for their school project. It was not a good day for the companies they picked. They needed to subtract these mixed numbers to calculate the new, lower value of their stocks.

a)   $48 - \dfrac{5}{16}$

b)   $28\dfrac{1}{4} - 13\dfrac{7}{8}$

GH-113. Ahmal was muttering about the work he had to do to calculate the stock losses when he looked up and saw that Kezer was already done.

"How did you finish so fast?" he asked.

"Easy," said Kezer.  "I used a shortcut."

"I could sure use a shortcut," sighed Ahmal.

If you know a shortcut, explain it to Ahmal; otherwise, read on.

"Look," said Kezer, "Two fractions that add up to 1 are complementary, like $\dfrac{3}{7}$ and $\dfrac{4}{7}$.

To do $48 - \dfrac{5}{16}$, just remember that the complementary fraction for $\dfrac{5}{16}$ is $\dfrac{11}{16}$ so

$48 - \dfrac{5}{16} = 47\dfrac{11}{16}$ ."

"Okay, I see that, but what about $28\dfrac{1}{4} - 13\dfrac{7}{8}$ ?" Ahmal asked.

"I just used a negative number," said Kezer.  "You just do the whole numbers and fractions separately and then put the results together like this:

$$28 - 13 = 15 \ \text{ and } \ \dfrac{1}{4} - \dfrac{7}{8} = \dfrac{2}{8} - \dfrac{7}{8} = -\dfrac{5}{8}, \ \text{ then } 15 + -\dfrac{5}{8} = 14\dfrac{3}{8} \ ."$$

GH-114. Use Kezer's method to calculate each difference.

a)   $97 - 26\dfrac{3}{5}$

b)   $100 - 50\dfrac{5}{6}$

c)   $12\dfrac{1}{4} - 15\dfrac{3}{4}$

d)   $33\dfrac{1}{3} - 25\dfrac{7}{12}$

GH-115. Follow your teacher's directions for practicing mental math. Record the solution you think you will use if there is another problem like this one.

GH-116.  Ahmal was thinking more about Malik's idea of using a Giant **1** to help divide and realized it could be taken still further. He used the problem $2\frac{1}{2} \div \frac{3}{4}$ to demonstrate his idea.

*Ahmal:*   I agree that $2\frac{1}{2} \div \frac{3}{4} = \dfrac{2\frac{1}{2}}{\frac{3}{4}} = \dfrac{\frac{5}{2}}{\frac{3}{4}}$. But let's not just use a regular Giant **1** like you did, let's use a Super Giant **1**!

*Malik:*   Show me what you mean.

Then Ahmal writes:   $\dfrac{\frac{5}{2}}{\frac{3}{4}} \cdot \dfrac{\frac{4}{3}}{\frac{4}{3}}$ .

a)   Complete Ahmal's problem by multiplying and then simplifying.

b)   Cheryl multiplied the fractions and got $\dfrac{\frac{20}{6}}{\frac{12}{12}}$. But then, she was stuck. "What should I do about the $\frac{12}{12}$?" she asked. Explain how she can finish the problem.

c)   Show how to write $\frac{4}{5} \div \frac{1}{2}$ Ahmal's way; then solve it using a Super Giant **1**.

GH-117.  Use a ruler to draw a picture of $5 \div \frac{2}{3}$ .

a)   Draw a line 5 inches long and then show how many $\frac{2}{3}$ inches are in 5 inches.

b)   Use Malik's method to verify your answer.

c)   Use Ahmal's method to verify your answer.

GH-118.  Solve each of the following problems using Ahmal's method.

a)   $\frac{2}{3} \div \frac{2}{5}$      b)   $\frac{5}{6} \div \frac{1}{12}$      c)   $3\frac{1}{8} \div 2\frac{1}{2}$

GH-119. Traniqua said, "I think I have an easy way to describe what we have been doing. For any problem where I need to divide a number—call it F—by a fraction $\frac{N}{D}$, I just multiply F by the reciprocal fraction $\frac{D}{N}$."

Ahmal said, "Oh, my method works because the top of my super fraction is the same as Traniqua's and we know that the product of the denominators is always 1 because of the number we choose for our Super Giant **1**. Let's just remember that it is 1 and that dividing by 1 does not change the answer. So we only need to worry about the numerators."

a) Make up two examples and use Traniqua's rule to do the divisions.

b) Traniqua had discovered what is usually called Invert and Multiply. What does the word "invert" mean here and what is inverted?

GH-120.

---

### DIVISION OF FRACTIONS

**Division of Fractions with a Super Giant 1 Method:**

$$F \div \frac{N}{D} = \frac{F}{\frac{N}{D}} \cdot \frac{\frac{D}{N}}{\frac{D}{N}} = \frac{F \cdot \frac{D}{N}}{1} = F \cdot \frac{D}{N}$$

$$\frac{3}{4} \div \frac{2}{5} = \frac{\frac{3}{4}}{\frac{2}{5}} \cdot \frac{\frac{5}{2}}{\frac{5}{2}} = \frac{\frac{3}{4} \cdot \frac{5}{2}}{1} = \frac{3}{4} \cdot \frac{5}{2} = \frac{15}{8}$$

OR

**Division of Fractions with the Invert and Multiply Method:**

$$F \div \frac{N}{D} = F \cdot \frac{D}{N}$$

Invert the divisor (switch the numerator and the denominator) and then multiply the fractions as usual.

$$\frac{3}{4} \div \frac{2}{5} = \frac{3}{4} \cdot \frac{5}{2} = \frac{15}{8}$$

---

Answer the questions below in your Tool Kit to the right of the double-lined box.

a) Use the Invert and Multiply Method to compute $\frac{3}{5} \div \frac{2}{3}$.

b) Use the Super Giant **1** Method to compute $2\frac{5}{8} \div \frac{3}{4}$.

-c) Which method is most comfortable for you? Why?

GH-121. At the Science Fair, 23 cakes were each cut into eight pieces and each piece was sold for $0.75. Half a cake remained at the end of the day. How much money did the school make selling cakes?

GH-122. Use any method to divide.

a) $\frac{3}{4} \div \frac{1}{6}$

b) $\frac{5}{12} \div \frac{1}{6}$

c) $\frac{2}{3} \div \frac{1}{2}$

d) $2\frac{2}{3} \div \frac{1}{2}$

GH-123. Solve the following problems without paper or pencil. Just write the answer but be ready to explain your thinking.

a) What is $2\frac{1}{2} \div \frac{1}{2}$?

b) What is $1\frac{2}{3} \div \frac{1}{3}$?

GH-124. A graph of seven coordinate points is shown below right.

a) Look at the points on the graph and write them into a table to organize them.

Example:

| x | -3 | -2 | -1 | 0 | 1 | 2 | 3 |
|---|----|----|----|---|---|---|---|
| y |    | 1  |    |   |   |   |   |

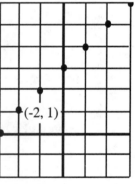

(-2, 1)

b) What algebraic rule created these points?

c) Name at least two other points which would follow this rule.

GH-125. Evaluate each expression below. You must do each problem in your head, without a pencil or paper. Be prepared to explain your method.

a) What is one-half of one-half?

b) What is one-half of one-tenth?

c) What is one-half of two-tenths?

d) What is one-tenth of one-tenth?

CHAPTER 7

GH-126. Howard went to the mall and saw a banner announcing, "ALL SPORTING GOODS: ONE-TENTH OFF!" He saw a pair of roller blade laces for $0.40. He wanted to find out how much money would be deducted from the $0.40 price. He knew that 0.40 equals 0.4, so he asked himself, "How much is $\frac{1}{10}$ of $\frac{4}{10}$?"

a) On your resource page of hundredths grids, lightly shade and label 0.4 or $\frac{4}{10}$ vertically, as shown at right in diagram (i).

b) Next, in the other direction, shade and darkly label $\frac{1}{10}$ of $\frac{4}{10}$ as shown at right in diagram (ii). What is the fraction of the grid that is darkly shaded? Do not reduce. What is the decimal equivalent of the part of the grid that is shaded?

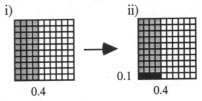

c) Write a fraction equation for this process.

d) Write a decimal equation for this process using the same form.

e) How much money will Howard save with the laces on sale?

GH-127. While in the sporting goods store, Howard found some new running shoes that weigh seven-tenths (or 70%) of the amount of his old running shoes. His old shoes weigh 0.8 kg. He asked himself, "How much is 0.7 of 0.8?"

a) On a hundredths grid, lightly shade 0.8 in one direction as shown at right. Finish the drawing by darkly shading 0.7 of it in the other direction.

b) Write a fraction equation for this problem. Label the answer with proper units.

c) Write a decimal equation for this problem. Label the answer with proper units.

d) Is your answer more or less than the old shoes' weight?

GH-128. For each of the following problems, use a hundredths grid diagram. Under each drawing, write both a fraction and a decimal equation.

a) (0.3)(0.6)     b) (0.5)(0.4)     c) (0.2)(0.7)

GH-129.  Use a generic rectangle drawing to multiply (2.3)(1.4).

a)  Draw and label the four sections as shown at right.

b)  Fill in the areas of the subproblems.

c)  Write an equation to find the total area.

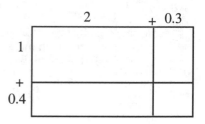

GH-130.  Draw generic rectangle diagrams and write equations to find the following products.

a)  (6.5)(4.7)

b)  (3.8)(4.4)

GH-131.  Howard, in his new lightweight running shoes, was able to walk at the rate of 0.83 meters per second. His coach timed him through a short distance for 12.2 seconds. How far did he walk during that time? Set up a proportion to answer this problem. Use paper and a pencil.

GH-132.  In decimal multiplication, the location of the decimal point in the answer is related to the location of the decimal points in the numbers in the problem.

a)  Write a fraction equation for (0.3)(0.16). Do not reduce your answer.

b)  Write this equation in decimal form.

c)  In this problem you multiplied tenths by hundredths to get thousandths. When the problem is written in decimals, describe the relationship between the number of decimal places in the parts of the problem and the number of decimal places in the answer.

d)  In problems GH-126 through GH-128 what was the total number of digits to the right of the decimal point in each of the numbers you multiplied? How many are to the right in each answer?

e)  Describe a shortcut for locating the decimal point in the answer of a decimal multiplication problem.

GH-133.

### MULTIPLYING DECIMAL NUMBERS

The answer to a multiplication problem is called the product of the factors.

To place the decimal point correctly in the product, count the decimal places in each of the factors and count that many places from the right in the product.

Examples:

one place  two places  three places
2.3   ·   5.06   =   11.638

1 + 2 places = 3 places
from the right

four places   two places   six places
0.0004   ·   3.42   =   0.001368

4 + 2 places = 6 places
from the right

one place   one place   two places
0.5   ·   0.2   =   0.10

1 + 1 places = 2 places
from the right

Answer the questions below in your Tool Kit to the right of the double-lined box.

a)  Show (2.3)(5.06) as a fraction multiplication problem and explain why the answer is in thousandths (three places).

b)  Show (0.004)(3.42) as a fraction multiplication problem and explain why the answer is in hundred-thousandths (five places).

GH-134.  Convert the fractions to decimals in the following problems. Indicate repeating decimals with a line over the repeat.

a)  $\frac{3}{4}$                    b)  $\frac{1}{8}$                    c)  $\frac{7}{10}$

d)  $\frac{4}{5}$                    e)  $\frac{8}{9}$                    f)  $\frac{22}{7}$

GH-135.  Mentally calculate the following products. Use the rule for decimal multiplication to write an equation in which the decimal point is written in the correct location.

a)  (0.4)(0.1)            b)  (0.3)(0.02)            c)  (0.7)(0.4)

d)  Stacey said, "Stephanie, look at my answer to part (c), $0.7 \cdot 0.4 = 0.28$. Usually when I multiply, I get a bigger answer than the numbers I start with. Twenty-eight hundredths, 0.28, is less that either 0.4 or 0.7. I must have made a mistake."

Stephanie responded, "Well, one-half times one-half is one-fourth, and one-fourth is less then one-half. I think when you multiply by a fraction or decimal less than one, you get less than what you started with."

Write a sentence or two about who you think is correct and why.

GH-136.   Complete the following Diamond Problems.

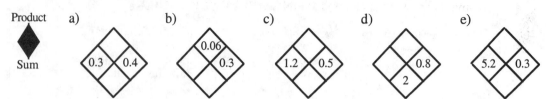

GH-137.   Create a table to organize a set of points which follow the rule $y = \frac{2}{3}x$. Graph the ordered pairs on a coordinate grid.

GH-138.   Follow your teacher's directions for practicing mental math.

GH-139.   Mr. Garcia needs to cut short pieces out of a 16-foot long two-by-four for spacers in the wall of his new house. He is going to make cuts across the length of the board. The blocks need to be one-half foot long. How many blocks can be made from this board? Pretend that the width of the saw blade is zero.

   a)   How many half-foot lengths are in 16 feet?

   b)   Write a division equation to show this idea.

GH-140.   Now we want to see how Mr. Garcia could have solved his problem using decimal division.

   a)   One way to solve Mr. Garcia's problem was to write the division as $\frac{16}{\frac{1}{2}}$. But we know $\frac{1}{2} = 0.5$, so we can also write the division problem as $\frac{16}{0.5}$. Multiply $\frac{16}{0.5}$ by the Giant 1 $\frac{10}{10}$ to change the fraction to a fraction which only has whole numbers. What do you get?

   b)   Notice that $\frac{160}{5}$ represents the same amount as $\frac{160}{5}$, so $0.5\overline{)16}$ has the same answer as $5\overline{)160}$. Many people have difficulty locating the decimal point in the answer to $0.5\overline{)16}$, but when the question is $5\overline{)160}$, few people have trouble locating the decimal point in the answer. Solve $\frac{16}{0.5}$ by calculating $5\overline{)160}$.

GH-141. Get a resource page from your teacher. Leave space to show all your work in each column where work is required. Do not use a calculator.

| | Decimal Division Problem | Multiply by Giant 1 | Whole Number Division Problem | Answer |
|---|---|---|---|---|
| Example | $\dfrac{2.5}{0.25}$ | $\dfrac{2.5}{0.25} \cdot \dfrac{100}{100} = \dfrac{250}{25}$ | $25\overline{)250}$ | 10 |
| | $\dfrac{1.4}{0.7}$ | $\dfrac{1.4}{0.7} \cdot \dfrac{10}{10} =$ | | |
| | $\dfrac{520}{0.013}$ | $\dfrac{520}{0.013} \cdot \dfrac{1000}{1000} =$ | | |
| | $8.2 \div 0.4$ | $\dfrac{8.2}{0.4} \cdot \dfrac{?}{?} =$ | | |
| | $0.02 \div 0.005$ | | | |
| | $10.05 \div 0.25$ | | | |

GH-142. Set up division problems with whole numbers as shown in the previous problem to help you solve the problems below. Show all your work.

a) $\dfrac{2.5}{0.25}$      b) $\dfrac{1.12}{0.7}$      c) $\dfrac{59.1}{0.3}$

GH-143.

### DIVIDING BY A DECIMAL NUMBER

When you are dividing by a decimal number, count how many digits the decimal point must move to the right to become an integer (whole number).

Then move the decimal point in the dividend the same direction and the same number of digits.

Example:

$$\text{divisor} \longrightarrow 4.07\overline{)8.30} \longleftarrow \text{dividend}$$

Moving the decimal point two places to the right is multiplying by both numbers by 100.

The Giant **1** (Identity Property) proves this.

$$8.3 \div 4.07 = \dfrac{8.3}{4.07} \cdot \dfrac{100}{100} = \dfrac{830}{407}$$

Choose either way to divide by a decimal number.

>>Problem continues on the next page.>>

Answer the questions below in your Tool Kit to the right of the double-lined box.

a) Which method would you choose?

b) Divide using the method you prefer: $15.75 \div 0.25$.

GH-144. Stuart is a plumber working on the Garcias' house. He is working with PVC pipe that has an internal diameter of $\frac{3}{4}$ inch. The thickness of the pipe is $\frac{3}{16}$ inch. What is the exterior diameter of the pipe?

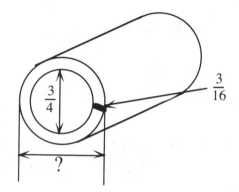

GH-145. Write an equation and solve the following problems. Give answers in decimal form.

a) What is the product of three-tenths and four-hundredths?

b) What is the sum of five and thirteen-hundredths plus twelve and six-tenths?

c) What is forty-seven and seven-tenths minus twenty-three and nineteen-hundredths?

d) What is the product of twenty-hundredths and sixty-five thousandths?

e) What is the sum of fourteen tenths and fourteen-hundredths?

GH-146. Each problem below has an error in the answer. Find the error, explain how to correct the mistake, and correct it. In parts (a) and (d), the x means to multiply.

a)
```
    10
  x 0.5
  -----
    50
```

b)
```
  467.92
 + 1.293
 -------
  479.85
```

c)
```
    100
 - 62.837
 --------
  38.837
```

d)
```
   1.234
 x 0.003
 -------
  0.3702
```

e)
```
  4006.3
 - 34.98
 -------
 3971.48
```

e)
```
    45.6
   32.87
 + 0.003
 -------
   374.6
```

GH-147. **Algebra Puzzles** Solve these equations.

a) $7\frac{2}{3} - 3x = -1\frac{1}{3}$

b) $-6\frac{2}{5} + 9x = 11\frac{3}{5}$

GH-148. Simplify.

a) (4.76)(12.5)

b) 45.6 + 23.68

c) 48 – 12.62

d) 10(0.034)

e) 368.9 – 234.78

f) 13.6 + 23.05 + 0.781

GH-149. Sandy needs to build an open box for a heating vent for the Garcias' house as shown in the drawing below. Remember to adjust for the overlap the way you did with the masking tape letters. The vent enclosure will be covered by a metal grate and has an open back.

Study the blueprint. Decide what sizes of plywood Sandy should cut. The plywood is $\frac{3}{4}$ of an inch thick.

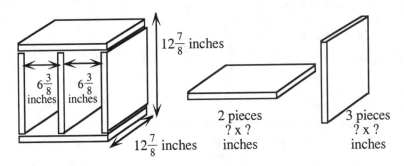

GH-150. Jake and his sister Erin bought some new pencils. They had three blue, five gold, four striped, and three green pencils. They decided to share their supplies. In order to be fair, they put all the supplies in a paper bag and drew out one item at a time.

a) What are Jake's chances of getting a green pencil on the first draw?

b) After Jake gets a green pencil, how many pencils remain in the bag?

c) If Jake got a green pencil on his first draw, what is the probability of him getting a striped pencil on his second draw?

GH-151. Calculate lengths a and b using Stuart's plumbing diagram. Remember that the pipe has a $1\frac{1}{8}$-inch exterior diameter.

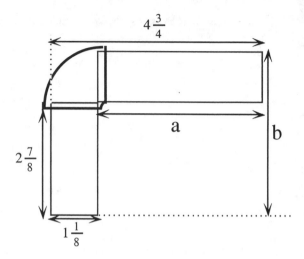

GH-152. **Chapter Summary** Take out a clean sheet of paper, fold it in half the long way, and then fold it in thirds the other way so that when you open the paper it looks like the one below.

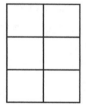

a) Check the Tool Kit list in problem GH-159 and enter each item from the list at the top of one of the boxes. Use both sides of your paper. Include the problem number for quick reference.

b) In each box show an example of each type of problem. You may make up your own problem, you may use one from the book, or you may borrow one from a teammate. Be sure to show the problem, the steps needed to solve it, and the answer.

c) As you do this, check with the others on your team to verify that each example is correct.

d) Rate yourself on how well you understand and can do each type of problem by putting a number from 1 to 5 in the lower right corner of each box and circling it. A rating of 1 means, "I still need to do a lot of work on this." A 5 means, "I understand this very well and can do this type of problem accurately."

e) In the empty box at the lower right corner on your second page, write "Pocket Summary for Fractions, Chapter 7" so that when you fold the paper into sixths, the label is on the outside.

The Garcias are about ready to purchase the floor coverings for their new house: tiles for the bathrooms, carpet for the living room, den, and bedrooms, and vinyl tile for the kitchen and laundry room. They also want a special tile for the entry way. They need to know the total area for each type of floor covering.

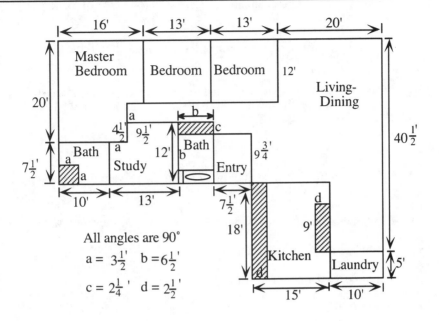

The following sequence of problems breaks this large problem into a series of subproblems.

GH-153.    First we will calculate the amount of tile needed for the two bathroom floors.

a)    Are both floors rectangles? Remember that you do not need tiles under the shower or the bath tub.

b)    Sketch and label a diagram for each bathroom floor.

c)    Calculate the area for each bathroom.

d)    What is the total area for the bathroom floors?

e)    What are the dimensions of the bathtub?

f)    The tiles the Garcias are planning to buy cost $3.60 per square foot.

g)    The sales tax is 7 percent. What is the cost of the tiles with tax added?

GH-154.  The vinyl tile for the kitchen and laundry room comes in one-foot squares.

a)   Sketch a diagram for the kitchen and for the laundry room.

b)   The vinyl tiles will cover the entire laundry room, but in the kitchen there are counters and built-in appliances so the tile is not needed for those areas that are shaded. Show your calculations to find the total area of the kitchen and laundry room floors.

c)   If vinyl tile costs $1.40 per square foot, how much will the tiles for the kitchen and laundry room cost?

d)   The Garcias heard that they could get a discount if they order 400 or more tiles. For 400 or more, the tiles will be 30% off the original price of $1.40 per square foot. Should they buy 400 tiles?

GH-155.  The Garcias will put the same kind of carpet in the two small bedrooms that they put in the study.

a)   Sketch diagrams for the two small bedrooms and the study with their dimensions.

b)   Calculate the areas of each room.

c)   Find the total area for the three rooms.

d)   If the carpeting costs $2.80 per square foot, how much will it cost to carpet the two bedrooms and the study?

GH-156.  The entry way will have special imported tiles.

a)   Sketch a diagram and label the dimensions for the entry way.

b)   Calculate the area.

c)   The tiles cost $5.20 per square foot. Write the area as a decimal and calculate the cost.

GH-157.  The carpet for the master bedroom is different than the other carpet.

a)   Draw a diagram for the master bedroom and label the dimensions.

b)   The carpet costs $3.84 per square foot and comes on a roll that is 8 feet wide. The Garcias decide to order two 20-foot pieces. Calculate the cost.

c)   How much did they have to cut out of one corner?

d)   How much did the extra corner cost them?

GH-158. The living room, dining room, and hallway areas are sketched at right and on the resource page.

You may cut the area into several rectangles and calculate the areas of all the parts or you may draw larger rectangles to enclose some parts and subtract. You may choose your own subproblems or follow the steps below.

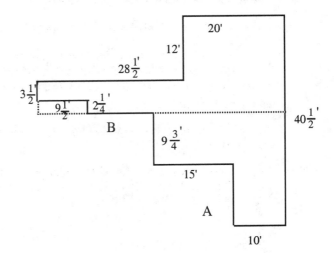

a) First find the missing dimensions A and B.

b) To calculate the area of the lower L shape at right, use the length A from part (a) to figure out length C.

c) Calculate the area of the whole rectangle and subtract the missing corner.

d) For the upper shape, show how to get D.

e) Find the area of the large outlined rectangle.

f) Sketch diagrams of the two rectangles you need to subtract. Find their areas.

g) Find the area of the shape in part (f).

h) Use your answers for parts (c) and (g) to get the total area that needs to be carpeted.

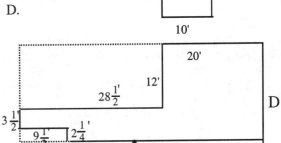

GH-159.   **What We Have Done in This Chapter**

Below is a list of the Tool Kit entries from this chapter.

- GH-19   Adding and Subtracting Fractions
- GH-33   Adding and Subtracting Mixed Numbers
- GH-58   Multiplying Two Fractions
- GH-62   Multiplying Mixed Numbers (also GH-65)
- GH-94   Reciprocals
- GH-120 Division of Fractions
- GH-133 Multiplying Decimal Numbers
- GH-143 Dividing by a Decimal Number

Review all the entries and read the notes you made in your Tool Kit. Make a list of any questions, terms, or notes you do not understand. Ask your partner or study team members for help. If anything is still unclear, ask your teacher.

# Mars Colony

Chapter 8

# Chapter 8
## *Mars Colony:* GEOMETRY, PROPERTIES, AND EQUATIONS

In this chapter you will generalize some of the methods you have learned for mental arithmetic. You will also learn about the properties and classifications of triangles and angles, and you will write and solve equations for a variety of situations.

In this chapter you will have the opportunity to:

- classify triangles by the lengths of their sides.

- solve angle problems involving complementary and supplementary angles.

- write and solve algebraic equations.

- solve problems by applying the Distributive, Associative, and Commutative Properties.

- combine like terms in algebraic expressions and equations.

Read the problem below, **but do not try to solve it now**. What you learn over the next few days will enable you to solve it.

MC-0. **Mars Colony**

The residents of the Mars Colony decided that they needed their own flag. They looked at all the existing flags and decided they wanted one that was unlike the flags of the larger nations. The flag at right is the one they chose.

The leaders of the colony want you to calculate each angle in the flag so that they can be faithfully reproduced.

| | |
|---|---|
| Number Sense | |
| Algebra and Functions | |
| Mathematical Reasoning | |
| Measurement and Geometry | |
| Statistics, Data Analysis, & Probability | |

# Chapter 8
*Mars Colony:* **GEOMETRY, PROPERTIES, AND EQUATIONS**

MC-1.    Today you will use your geometry vocabulary resource pages to play Polygon Grido.
Fill in a Polygon Grido card with words selected from the following vocabulary list.

| | |
|---|---|
| **Angles** | acute angle, right angle, obtuse angle, vertical angles |
| **Triangles** | acute triangle, right triangle, obtuse triangle, scalene triangle, isosceles triangle, equilateral triangle |
| **Quadrilaterals** | trapezoid, parallelogram, rectangle, rhombus, square |
| **Polygons** | polygon, regular polygon, quadrilateral, pentagon, hexagon, octagon, vertex, diagonal |
| **Other Terms** | circle, parallel lines, perpendicular lines, line segment, ray, base, height |

---

**Polygon Grido**
*A vocabulary game for the class.*

**Mathematical Purpose:** To review and develop geometric vocabulary.

**Object:** To cover the four corners or to get five markers in a row (vertically, horizontally, or diagonally).

**Materials:** Grido cards, markers, and vocabulary list.

**How to Play the Game:**
- Put a different vocabulary word in each cell on your Grido card before the game begins.
- A clue card will be shown.  Place a marker over a word on your card which correctly describes the clue.

**Ending the Game:** When someone covers four corners or gets five markers in a row, he or she should raise a hand.  When the words have been verified by the caller, the winner is declared.

---

After you play the game, write down at least five vocabulary words you plan to study before you play again.

MC-2.  Angles are classified by <u>how much the sides are opened, not</u> by how long the sides are. For example, clocks of different sizes show the same time. Even though the hands are longer on one clock, the angle is the same (as shown at right).

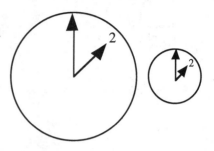

---

**TYPES OF ANGLES**

Clocks can help you understand angle classification. When a clock shows 3 o'clock or 9 o'clock, the hands make an angle of 90° or a **RIGHT ANGLE**.

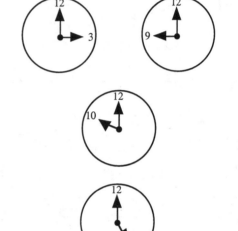

Angles that measure more than 0° but less than 90° are called **ACUTE ANGLES**.

Angles that measure more than 90° but less than 180° are called **OBTUSE ANGLES**.

Angles that measure 180° are called **STRAIGHT ANGLES**.

---

To the right of the double-lined box in your Tool Kit, sketch and label an example of an acute angle, an obtuse angle, a right angle, and a straight angle.

MC-3. Ten o'clock is an example of an acute angle, 5 o'clock is an example of an obtuse angle, and 6 o'clock is an example of a straight angle. Classify each angle described below as either acute, right, obtuse, or straight.

a) The angle formed by the hands of a clock at 8 o'clock.

b) The angle formed by the hands of a clock at 1 o'clock.

c) The angle formed by the hands of a clock at 2:25.

d) The angle formed by the hands of a clock at 10:21.

MC-4. We usually measure angles in degrees. Before we measure an angle we compare it to a 90° right angle and classify it.

a) What is the measure of half of a right angle?

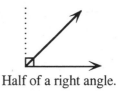

Half of a right angle.

b) If the angle at right is made with a right angle added to half of a right angle, what is its measure?

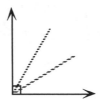

c) Suppose a right angle is divided into three equal angles as shown at right. What is the measure of each angle?

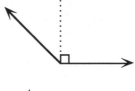

MC-5. Which is the best estimate for the measure of the angle at right?

(A) 80°        (B) 100°        (C) 90°        (D) 4°

MC-6. Which is the best estimate for the measure of the angle at right?

(A) 15°        (B) 95°        (C) 160°        (D) 60°

MC-7. Which is the best estimate for the measure of the angle at right?

(A) 90°        (B) 150°        (C) 30°        (D) 80°

MC-8. A polygon can be referred to by its vertices such as quadrilateral FRED at right.

a) What kind of quadrilateral is FRED?

b) Which angles are obtuse?

c) Which angles are acute?

MC-9. Heidi thought of a number. She divided it by 4. Her answer is 28.

   a)  Write an equation for Heidi's number.

   b)  Solve your equation.

   c)  What was Heidi's original number?


MC-10. Toño thought of a number. He multiplied it by 7 and then subtracted 25. His answer is 10.

   a)  Write an equation for Toño's number.

   b)  Solve the equation you wrote.

   c)  What is Toño's original number?


MC-11. A Martian Jetcopter has space for 8 people. One Jetcopter is filled and departs every 2 minutes. You get in line at 10:28 a.m. as the first Jetcopter leaves. If there are 68 people in line ahead of you, at what time will your Jetcopter leave?

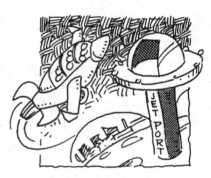


MC-12. Answer these questions using the flow diagram below.

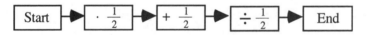

| Start | $\cdot \ \frac{1}{2}$ | $+ \ \frac{1}{2}$ | $\div \ \frac{1}{2}$ | End |

   a)  If you start with 9, with what number do you end?

   b)  If you start with -5, with what number do you end?

   c)  If you start with 0, with what number do you end?

   d)  If you end with 12, with what number did you start?

   e)  If you start with any number, how much larger is the ending number?


CHAPTER 8

MC-13. Calculate lengths a, b, and c using Stuart's plumbing diagram below. All pipes have an exterior diameter of $1\frac{1}{8}$ inches.

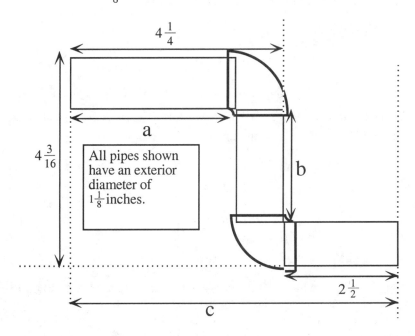

MC-14. Stuart the plumber buys pipe in 10-foot lengths.

a) How many inches of pipe are in one 10-foot length?

b) How many $24\frac{1}{2}$ -inch sections of pipe can Stuart cut from a 10-foot length? How many inches will remain?

c) If Stuart starts with a 10-foot length, cuts $24\frac{1}{2}$ inches, cuts $29\frac{7}{8}$ inches, and then cuts a four-foot length, how many inches will he have left?

MC-15. Now that we have started a new chapter, it is time for you to organize your binder.

a) Put the work from the last chapter in order and keep it in a separate folder.

b) When this is completed, write, "I have organized my binder."

MC-16.    Suppose we want to measure the angle at right.  To
          do so, we use a protractor.  Protractors <u>measure</u> <u>the</u>
          <u>spread</u>, using degrees, between the sides of an angle.

          Read Steps 1 through 5 below and refer to the
          diagrams that follow.

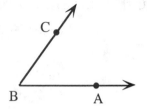

Step 1    Classify the angle—acute, obtuse, or right—so you know what a reasonable
          answer will be.

Step 2    Place the centering point of a protractor at the angle's vertex, point B.

Step 3    Line up one of the zero marks of the protractor with one ray of the angle, in
          this case $\overrightarrow{BA}$ (there is a zero on both sides of the protractors below because
          there are two scales).

Step 4    Count up from zero degrees to the point on the protractor where $\overrightarrow{BC}$ crosses
          it. (You may have to make $\overrightarrow{BC}$ longer.)

Step 5    Be sure that the answer is reasonable and the measure makes sense for the
          angle classification that you originally made.

If your protractors are too big for the illustrated angles, put the edge of a sticky note on
the side of the angle you are measuring to extend the side so you can read its
measurement.

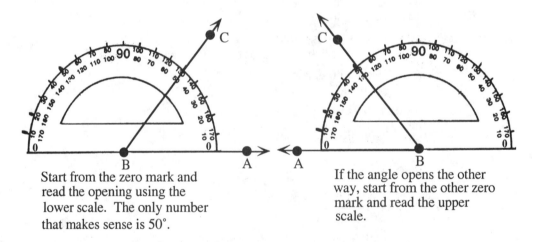

Start from the zero mark and           If the angle opens the other
read the opening using the             way, start from the other zero
lower scale.  The only number          mark and read the upper
that makes sense is 50°.               scale.

Copy this information into your notes to show that you have measured the acute angle
ABC.  Write it in the form "m∠ABC = 50°."  Why does the mark at 130° not make
sense for this angle?

MC-17.   Obtain a resource page from your teacher.

a)   Classify each angle on the resource page.

b)   Measure each angle with a protractor. If the sides of the angle are not long enough to reach the edge of your protractor, extend the rays on the resource page with a straightedge.

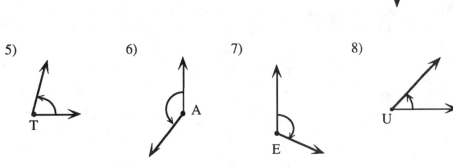

1)          2)          3)          4)

5)          6)          7)          8)

MC-18.   Use your protractor to draw angles with the following measures.

a)   45°          b)   30°          c)   110°          d)   160°

MC-19.   Use your straightedge to draw two intersecting lines like those shown below. Draw the lines much longer than the ones pictured.

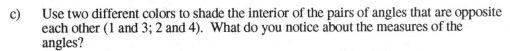

a)   Measure the size of each of the four angles.

b)   What is the name for the angles opposite each other in this figure?

c)   Use two different colors to shade the interior of the pairs of angles that are opposite each other (1 and 3; 2 and 4). What do you notice about the measures of the angles?

d)   Draw a second pair of lines intersecting at different angles. Measure the four angles. Shade the angles opposite each other. What do you notice about the measure of these angles?

MC-20.    Use your straightedge to draw a line (straight angle).  Put a
point on the line.  From that point, draw a ray to create two
angles like those shown at right.

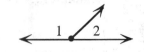

a)    Measure the size of each angle.

b)    Add the measurements of the two angles.  What is their sum?

c)    When the sum of the measures of two angles adds up to the measure of a straight
angle, they are called **supplementary angles**.  How many degrees are in a straight
angle?  Check with your protractor.

d)    Are the angles you drew supplementary?  Explain how you know.


MC-21.    Measure and draw a 90° angle.  Draw a ray to split the angle into
two parts as shown at right.  This is a pair of **complementary
angles**.

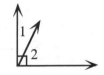

a)    Measure the number of degrees in each of the angles.  Be
accurate when you measure.

b)    What is the sum of the measures of angles 1 and 2?

# PROPERTIES OF ANGLE PAIRS

Intersecting lines form four angles.  The pairs of angles across from each other are called **VERTICAL ANGLES**.  The measures of vertical angles are equal.

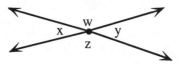

∠x and ∠y are vertical angles
∠w and ∠z are vertical angles

If the sum of the measures of two angles is exactly 180°, then they are called **SUPPLEMENTARY ANGLES**.

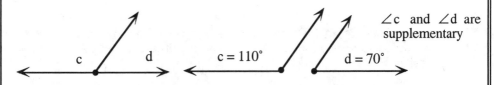

∠c  and  ∠d are supplementary

If the sum of the measures of two angles is exactly 90°, then they are called **COMPLEMENTARY ANGLES**.

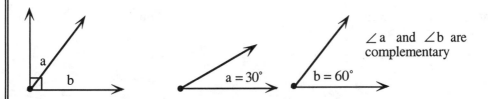

∠a  and  ∠b are complementary

Angles that share a vertex and one side but have no common interior points (that is, do not overlap each other) are called **ADJACENT ANGLES**.

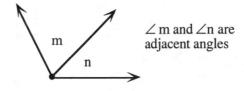

∠m and ∠n are adjacent angles

Make these notes in your Tool Kit to the right of the double-lined box.

For each type of angle pair, write a note that will help you remember the name.

MC-23.    Complementary and supplementary angles do not have to be adjacent. Use your Properties of Angle Pairs Tool Kit to help you classify the following pairs of angles as complementary, supplementary, adjacent, or vertical.

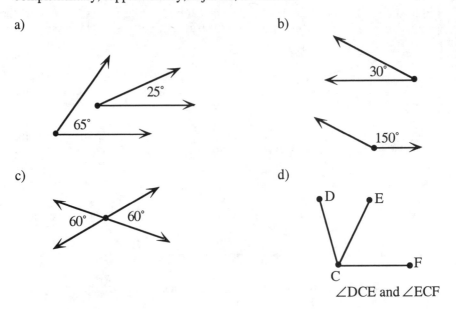

a)

b)

c)

d)

∠DCE and ∠ECF

MC-24.    Find the value of each variable in the following figures. Do not use a protractor. Use the properties of angles to help you.

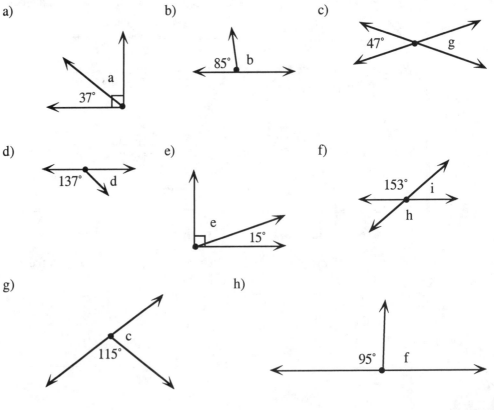

a)

b)

c)

d)

e)

f)

g)

h)

**MC-25.**

### NAMING ANGLES

There are several ways to label and refer to the angles in a geometric figure. When an angle is alone we may name it ∠1, ∠A, ∠CAB, or ∠BAC.

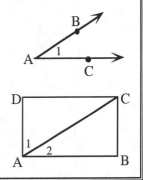

When an angle is part of a diagram, using just one letter may be confusing. There are three angles with vertex A. You can always use three points to name each angle: ∠DAB, ∠CAB, and ∠DAC. Notice the vertex is always the middle letter. Two of the angles can also be named by number: ∠DAC = ∠1; ∠CAB = ∠2.

Make these notes in your Tool Kit to the right of the double-lined box.

a) Assume the figure in the Tool Kit is a rectangle. What is the measure of ∠DAB?

b) Choose two colors. Shade ∠DAC with one color and ∠CAB with the other. Make a note of which color goes with which angle.

**MC-26.** Obtain a resource page from your teacher. Use your protractor to measure the angles on your resource page.

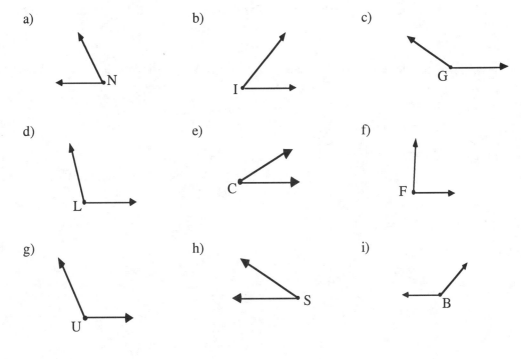

a)

b)

c)

d)

e)

f)

g)

h)

i)

**>>Problem continues on the next page.>>**

Mars Colony: Geometry, Properties, and Equations

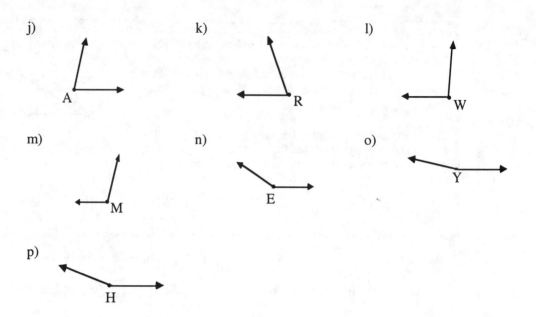

j)

k)

l)

m)

n)

o)

p)

MC-27.   Two angles are complementary.  If one measures 65°, what is the measure of the other angle?

MC-28.   Two angles are supplementary.  If one measures 125°, what is the measure of the other angle?

MC-29.   Two angles are vertical.  If one measures 63°, what is the measure of the other angle?

MC-30.   Find the area of each figure.

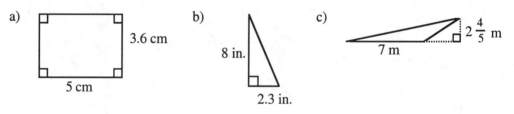

a)   3.6 cm   5 cm

b)   8 in.   2.3 in.

c)   7 m   $2\frac{4}{5}$ m

MC-31.   For each diagram below, identify each set of angles as complementary, supplementary, or vertical. Then use what you know about the properties of angles to find the measure of each angle labeled with a variable.

a)

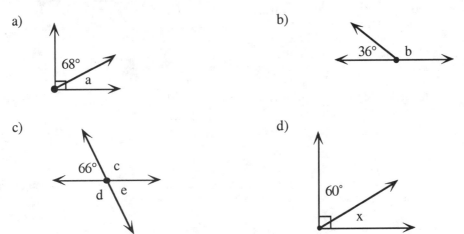

b)

c)

d)

MC-32.   Margaret and Claire were shopping. Margaret bought a $70 coat at 30% off and an $80 pair of shoes at 40% off. Claire bought a $70 pair of shoes at 40% off and an $80 coat at 30% off. Who spent more? How much more?

MC-33.   Bev was playing golf at the nine-hole Martian Red Rock Golf Course, where all the holes are par 3. (This means that the average player takes three swings or strokes to get the ball in the hole.) She took five strokes on the first hole, four strokes on the second, and three strokes on the third. Can she be at par (an average of three strokes) after the fourth hole? Explain.

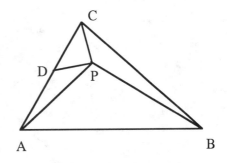

MC-34.   What is the sale price of a phone that is regularly priced at $95 if it is offered for 20% off?

MC-35.   Name three angles with a vertex at P.

MC-36. Your teacher will give you a picture rumored to have
been found in a cave on Mars. Do not let your
partner see it! You will describe the picture to your
partner who is back on Mars at Station Omega. You
may not see what your partner is drawing until the
picture is finished. Your partner must draw the
picture based only on the directions you give. Use
precise mathematical vocabulary.

MC-37. When both you and your partner have completed your drawings based on the others'
directions, answer these questions.

a) How does your picture compare with the original?

b) List three vocabulary words that were useful for you.

c) List three vocabulary words your partner used which were not helpful.

MC-38. The diagrams below show some students' incorrect use of protractors. Explain what
each student needs to do to get the correct angle measure.

a)

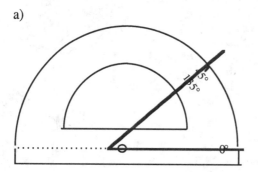

b)

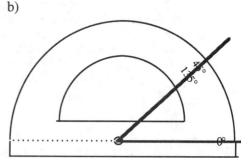

The student says that this is a 135° angle.

c)

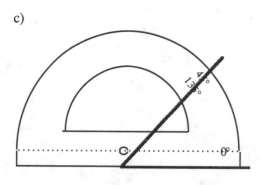

d)

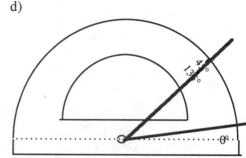

MC-39.   Obtain a resource page from your teacher.

a)   Measure the size of the angles in each of the triangles on your resource page.

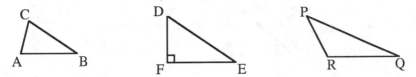

b)   Record the measures of each angle then calculate their sums in a chart like the one below.

| Triangle | $\triangle ABC$ | $\triangle PQR$ | $\triangle DEF$ |
|----------|-----------------|-----------------|-----------------|
| Angle | $m\angle A =$ | $m\angle P =$ | $m\angle D =$ |
| Angle | $m\angle B =$ | $m\angle Q =$ | $m\angle E =$ |
| Angle | $m\angle C =$ | $m\angle R =$ | $m\angle F =$ |
| Sum | | | |

MC-40.   You will need your protractor and a centimeter ruler.

a)   Draw an angle with a measure of 60° and mark a point on <u>each</u> ray 6 centimeters from the vertex.

b)   Connect the two points you marked in part (a) and measure the distance between them in centimeters.

c)   Find the perimeter of the triangle you just created.

d)   What are the measures of the other two angles of your triangle?

e)   What kind of triangle is it?

MC-41.   Two straight lines intersect. Angles A and C are vertical angles. Angle A measures 40°. Angle C measures four times some number of degrees plus 4°.

a)   Write an equation using x.

b)   Solve for x. Show all your steps.

MC-42.    Write equations and solve them to find the values of the variables in the diagrams below.
          The solutions in part (a) are given so you can see what is expected.

a)

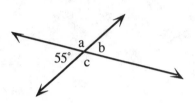

a + 55° = 180°, so a = 125°
b = 55°
c = 125°

b)

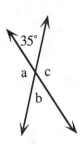

c)

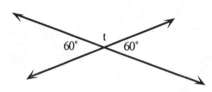

d)

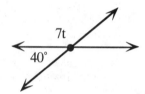

e)    These angles are complementary.

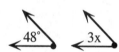

f)

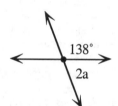

g)    These angles are supplementary.

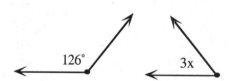

h)

MC-43.    If necessary, insert parentheses in each problem to make the equation true.

a)    $4 \cdot 2 + 8 = 40$

b)    $6 + 3 \cdot 5 = 45$

c)    $8 \cdot 6 + 3 \cdot 10 = 78$

d)    $8 \div 4 - 2 \cdot 7 = 28$

**MC-44.** Find the area and perimeter of each shape below. Show all of your subproblems.

a) All angles are right angles.

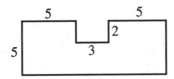

b) An isosceles trapezoid with a rectangular piece cut out.

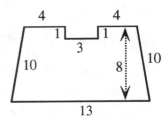

**MC-45.** Harvey, the great white rabbit, was out stargazing. His lunch bag was filled with 10 carrots and 17 parsnips.

a) What is the probability that when he reaches in for his next treat, he will pull out a parsnip?

b) If he pulled out a parsnip for his first treat, what is the probability that when he reaches in for his second treat, he will pull out another parsnip?

**MC-46.** Find the size of each missing angle without measuring.

a)

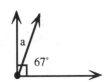

b)

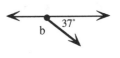

**MC-47.** Simplify each of the following fractions.

a) $3\frac{2}{3} + 4\frac{7}{8}$

b) $\frac{5}{6} \cdot 1\frac{1}{5}$

c) $2\frac{1}{4} - \frac{5}{6}$

d) $4\frac{1}{3} \div \frac{2}{3}$

MC-48.   Write and solve a proportion to answer the following question.

Georgina has decided that 35% of everything she eats will be fruit. If Georgina regularly eats about 22 pounds of food each week, how many of those pounds must be fruit?

MC-49.   A polygon is shown at right.

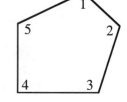

a)   Based on the number of sides, name the polygon.

b)   Classify each of the five angles as acute, obtuse, right, or straight.

c)   Would it be possible for a pentagon to have four right angles? If so draw a picture. If not, why not?

d)   Could a pentagon have three right angles? If so draw a picture. If not, why not?

MC-50.   On a balance scale, Xan needs three 6-centimeter by 6-centimeter tiles and eight 3-centimeter by 3-centimeter tiles to balance with some 2-centimeter by 2-centimeter tiles. How many of the smaller tiles does he need if all of them are the same thickness?

MC-51.   Follow your teacher's instructions for practicing mental math.

MC-52.  Tsaan Fou said that the sum of the measures of the angles in any triangle is always the
        same, no matter what kind of triangle it is.  Is this true?  Follow the procedure below to
        investigate this relationship.

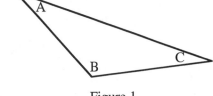

a)  Use a ruler to draw a large triangle with one base
    on the edge of a half sheet of paper.  Be sure to
    make your triangle a different shape than the one
    shown at right and different from your
    teammates' triangles.

b)  Color each angle a different color.  Write the
    letters A, B, and C inside each angle because you
    are going to cut them out.  (See Figure 1.)

Figure 1

c)  Cut out the triangle.

d)  Trace your triangle in your notebook.

e)  Label the vertices of this traced triangle the same
    way as the original vertices were labeled.

Figure 2

f)  Below the tracing in your notebook, use a ruler to
    draw a straight line.  Put a small dot on this line
    near the middle.  (See Figure 2.)  What is
    the measure of this straight angle?

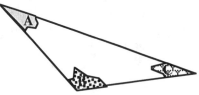

g)  Now carefully tear the corners off your triangle
    so that they include the letters.  (See Figure 3.)

Figure 3

h)  Arrange the torn corners on the straight line
    without any overlap to see what happens.
    (See Figure 4.)  Try the angles in different
    arrangements.  Does the order of the angles
    change the sum of their measurements?

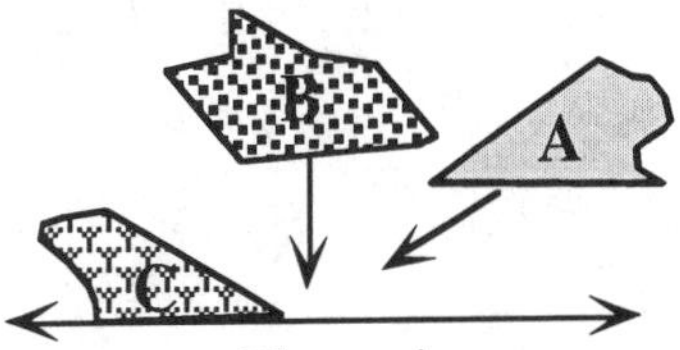

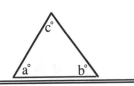

i)  Tape the three corners on the line in your
    notebook.  Also tape the remainder of the torn
    triangle inside the tracing of it in your notebook.

Figure 4

j)  Write a sentence to summarize the findings of your investigation.

MC-53.

### ANGLES IN A TRIANGLE

The sum of the measures of the **angles in any triangle**
is exactly 180°.

For any triangle, $a° + b° + c° = 180°$.

Make these notes in your Tool Kit to the right of the
double-lined box.

Sketch a triangle like the one at right and write an
equation showing the sums of the measures of its angles.

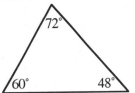

MC-54.   Find the measure of the missing angle in each picture below.

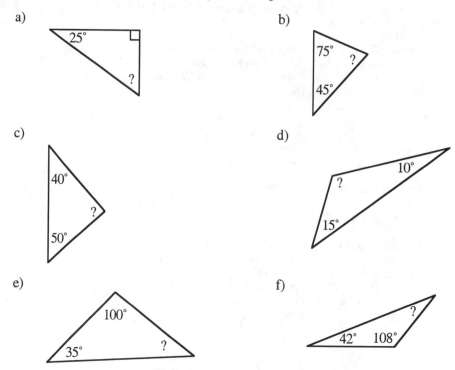

a)

b)

c)

d)

e)

f)

MC-55.   Juvenita wondered whether the same thing would be true for quadrilaterals. Would the sum of the measures of the four angles always turn out to be the same? Investigate by following a procedure similar to what you did for the triangles.

a)   Each team member should use a ruler to draw a different quadrilateral.

b)   Label and color the angles inside the figure.

c)   Sketch a similar quadrilateral on your paper and label the angles in the same order.

d)   Tear off the four corners, fit them together around a point with no overlap, and tape them on your paper.

e)   What did you find? Write a statement to summarize what you observed about the sum of the angles in a quadrilateral.

MC-56.   Derrick has another way to show that the measures of the angles of a quadrilateral add up to 360°. He says you can just draw a diagonal to make two triangles.

a)   Draw a quadrilateral.

b)   Draw a diagonal of the quadrilateral. What geometric figures do you have inside the quadrilateral?

c)   What is the sum of the measures of the angles of each triangle?

d)   Explain how Derrick could use the two triangles to show that the sum of the measures of the angles in a quadrilateral is 360°.

MC-57.

## ANGLES IN A QUADRILATERAL

The sum of the measures of the angles in a quadrilateral is exactly 360°.

In general, for any quadrilateral,
$a° + b° + c° + d° = 360°$.

Make these notes in your Tool Kit to the right of the double-lined box.

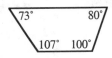

Copy the quadrilateral at right and write an equation to show the sum of its angles.

MC-58.    Draw a triangle that has an interior angle with a measure of 30° between two sides that are 9 centimeters and 8 centimeters long. Complete the third side by connecting the endpoints of the lengths you just drew. Measure the length of the third side. Measure the other two angles and find the perimeter of the triangle you drew.

MC-59.    Joe has a collection of 80 CDs. He has 30 country, 10 soundtracks, 25 oldies, and 15 rap CDs. He listens to each type of music equally.

a)    What is the probability Joe will be listening to oldies?

b)    What is the probability he will be listening to soundtracks or oldies?

c)    What is the probability he will be listening to rap?

d)    If Joe gives away all his soundtracks, what is the probability he will be listening to rap?

MC-60.    For each of the figures, find the missing angle.

a)

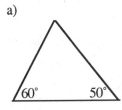

b)

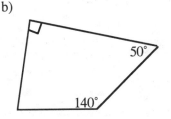

c)

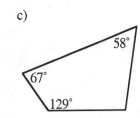

MC-61. Complete the following Diamond Problems.

Product

Sum

a)

$1\frac{1}{2}$  $2\frac{3}{4}$

b)

0.5

36.5

c)

5.4

54

d)

24

48

MC-62. Gertrude and Filomena Fibonacci are Mars colonists. Filomena, Gertrude's daughter, only weighs half as much as her mother.

a) On Earth, Gertrude and Filomena's weights add up to 180 pounds. Use a Guess and Check table to find out how much Filomena Fibonacci weighs.

b) Martian gravity is only 38% of Earth's gravity. What is Gertrude's weight on Mars?

MC-63. Create a table to organize a set of points which follow the rule $y = \frac{3}{2}x - \frac{1}{2}$. Graph the ordered pairs on a coordinate grid.

MC-64. Here is a graphical look at proportions and percents. Copy and complete the table below.

| Picture | Problem in Words / Proportion | Answer |
|---|---|---|
| Sketch the picture and fill in the missing parts. 5365 ⎤ n% / 4292 ⎤ 100% / 0 ⎦ 0% | What percent of 4292 is 5365? ——— = ——— | |
| n ⎤ 100% / 70.5 ⎦ 10% / 0 ⎦ 0% | State the question in words. ——— = ——— | |

MC-65. Farmer Bob of the Martian Colony counted his sheep and chickens in an unusual way. When he finished, he reported that he had counted 86 feet and 26 heads. Use a Guess and Check table to find how many sheep and chickens he owns

MC-66. Charles needs to find the size of the angles between the roads connecting the three colonies, but he does not have a protractor. All Charles has is a wedge with a fixed angle similar to the one at right. When he is in Mars Station Omega, Charles finds that the wedge fits in the angle created by the roads to the other two cities exactly two times. The same wedge fits the angle at Mars Station Gamma exactly seven times and exactly three times at Mars Station Alpha. Let x represent the measure of the angle of the wedge. Write an equation and find the measure of each angle.

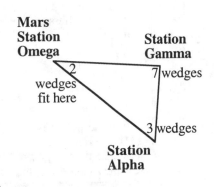

**Mars Station Omega**

**Station Gamma**

2 wedges fit here

7 wedges

3 wedges

**Station Alpha**

MC-67. Use your knowledge of geometry to write an equation for each of the following pictures. If possible, combine like terms. Then solve each equation for the variable and find the number of degrees in each angle.

a)

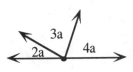

b)

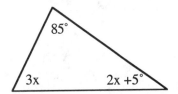

MC-68.

## CLASSIFYING TRIANGLES BY SIDE LENGTH

### Isosceles Triangle

A triangle with at least two congruent sides is called an **ISOSCELES TRIANGLE.** We know that the triangle at right is isosceles because the two sides have the same label, a. The single slash on each side is another way to indicate that the two sides are congruent.

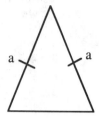

### Equilateral Triangle

A triangle with all three of its sides congruent is called an **EQUILATERAL TRIANGLE.** We know that the triangle at right is equilateral because the three sides have the same label, a, and the same number of slash marks.

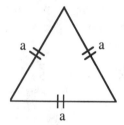

### Scalene Triangle

A triangle with no congruent sides is called a **SCALENE TRIANGLE.** The different number of marks on each side indicates that no pair of sides has the same length. Usually, a scalene triangle will have no marks at all.

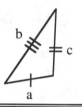

Make these notes in your Tool Kit to the right of the double-lined box.

a) Suppose one side of an equilateral triangle is 20 cm long. How long are the other sides?

b) Suppose two sides of an isosceles triangle are 8 cm and 11 cm. How long could the third side be?

MC-69. Use the perimeter of each triangle below to: (1) write an equation for each; (2) solve your equation; and (3) state the length of each side.

a) p = 122 cm

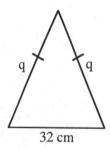

32 cm

b) p = 51.2 cm

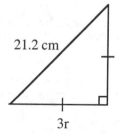

21.2 cm

3r

**>>Problem continues on the next page.>>**

CHAPTER 8

c)    p = 23"

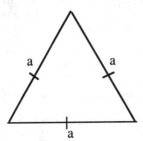

d)    p = 180"

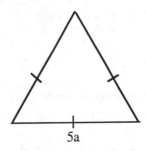

e)    p = 80"

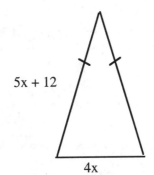

f)    p = 71"

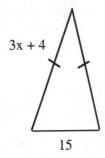

MC-70.    On Mars there are two kinds of money used in stores, Martian gips and Earth dollars. Heidi had 6 gips (6G) and $2, Carolan had 4 gips (4G) and $6, while Kaye had 20 gips (20G) and $15.

a)    How many gips did they have in all?

b)    How many Earth dollars did they have in all?

c)    What is  6G + $2 + 4G + $6 + 20G + $15?  (How much money do they have in all?)

d)    Two years ago a gip was worth $1.30.  How much money (in Earth dollars) would they have had then?

e)    Today a Martian gip is only worth $0.90 in Earth dollars.  What is the value of their money in Earth dollars today?

f)    When you determine how much money they have in all, you cannot just add the numbers of gips and dollars.  Why not?  Explain.

MC-71.    In the previous problem we **combined like terms**.  Terms with the same variables, such as Gips (or Gs), are called **like terms**.  Simplify the following problems by combining like terms.

a)    3G + 8G + 7G

b)    4G + 5 + 9

c)    2G + 5 + 9 + 7G

d)    6G + 4 + 12G + 8

MC-72. A family of Mars travelers decided to purchase a Mars Scooter which cost $157 in Earth dollars. When they pooled their Gips and dollars they had just enough money. (There is no sales tax on Mars.) Bob had 50 Gips and 18 dollars, Kris had 40 Gips, and Janelle had 30 Gips and 7 dollars. Write an equation and solve it to find out what a Gip was worth in Earth dollars that day.

MC-73.

> ## GUIDELINES FOR COMBINING LIKE TERMS
>
> **TERMS** are separated by addition or subtraction symbols.
>
> **LIKE TERMS** are terms that have the same variable or variables, such as 2G and 3G, 4x and 5x, $6y^2$ and $2y^2$, and 3xy and -2xy.
>
> Like terms such as 2G and 3G can be combined into one term by addition or subtraction so $2G + 3G = 5G$. Similarly, $4x + 5x = 9x$, $6y^2 - 2y^2 = 4y^2$, and $3xy - 2xy = xy$.
>
> The terms 2G and 3N must remain separate terms as $2G + 3N$ because G and N are different variables and can represent different numbers. Similarly, 5x and $6y^2$ cannot be combined, nor can 5x and 3xy.

Make these notes in your Tool Kit to the right of the double-lined box.

a) Write the expressions $3x + y$ and $3xy$.

b) Evaluate each expression using 5 for x and -2 for y.

c) What did you notice about the answers?

MC-74. **Algebra Puzzles** First combine like terms and then solve these equations.

a) $2G + 4 + 4G = 58$    b) $5x + 6 + 2x = 62$

c) $4x + 9 + 6 = 71$    d) $3x + 7 + 12 = 100$

MC-75. Jared says he can simplify $3x - 2y$ and get xy. He is mistaken. Explain to Jared why the two expressions are not equivalent. Choosing some numbers and substituting them into each expression may help to convince him.

MC-76. Use your knowledge of angles to write an equation for the following problems. Then solve each equation for the variable(s).

a)

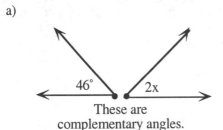

These are complementary angles.

b)

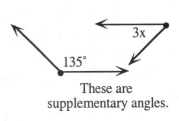

These are supplementary angles.

c)

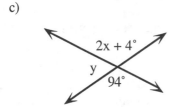

d)

MC-77. For the football game party, Jon's mother put out a large tray of peanut butter pretzels for people to eat. Jon's brother, Brian, ate half of the pretzels. His sister, Margaret, ate eight of them. His father, Al, claimed he did not like pretzels, but Jon counted and discovered his father had eaten 6 of them. Only 10 were left for Jon. How many pretzels did his mother put out at the beginning of the game?

a) Write an equation.

b) Solve it to answer the question.

MC-78. Simplify each expression.

a) $12 \cdot (-5)$     b) $-5 + (-16)$     c) $-24 - (-15)$     d) $-125 \div (-5)$

e) $156 \div (-12)$     f) $27 + (-19)$     g) $-18 - 32$     h) $-9 \cdot (-16)$

MC-79. In Charles' bag of golf balls, he has four that are white and eleven that are neon yellow. If he does not look in the bag, what is the probability that he will pull out a white ball on the first try?

MC-80. There is a flight control tower above Mars Station Omega that leans slightly to the left. Charles needs to know how many degrees the crooked control tower is leaning. He finds a wooden wedge that fits 17 times into the angle that the left side of the tower makes with the ground. He measures the angle on the right side of the wall with the same wedge and finds it fits nineteen times.

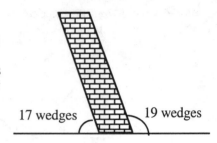

17 wedges    19 wedges

a) Write an equation to find the size of each of the angles.

b) Solve your equation to find the size of the wedge.

c) Determine the angle on each side. Do not forget to write your answer as a complete sentence.

MC-81. Xyrus and Katrina were arguing over the answer to a homework problem. Xyrus stated that $5 + 3 \cdot 6 = 23$. Katrina was sure the answer was 48. Who is correct and why?

MC-82. Brian is twice as old as Judy. Judy is five years younger than Tom. Tom is 15 years old. How old is Brian?

MC-83. Ronald buys a $0.75 soda and a $1.50 corn dog for lunch. He buys the same lunch for each of his two nephews. If he leaves a 20% tip, how much money does he spend?

MC-84. On a separate sheet of paper, use a ruler to draw a line segment 10 cm long. Label the end points with A and B.

a) Using point A as a vertex, use your protractor to draw a 60° angle.

b) Measure 10 cm along the upper ray of the angle, then mark and label point C.

c) Use your ruler to connect C with B.

d) Measure segment BC.

e) What kind of triangle is this?

f) Write A, B, and C inside their angles and carefully cut out the triangle.

g) Fold it in half so ∠A matches ∠B. What is true about ∠A and ∠B?

h) Now fold it the other way so ∠C matches ∠B. What is true about all three angles?

MC-85. Start with a line segment 10 cm long. Label the endpoints D and E.

a) Using point D as a vertex, use your protractor to draw a 52° angle.

b) Now draw a 52° angle using E as a vertex.

c) Extend the sides until they meet, and label that point F.

d) Measure the lengths of sides DF and EF to the nearest centimeter.

e) What do you notice about the sides? What kind of triangle is this?

MC-86.

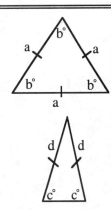

**ANGLES IN EQUILATERAL TRIANGLES**

In an equilateral triangle, all three angles are congruent and each measures 60°. Thus, m∠b = 60°

**ANGLES IN ISOSCELES TRIANGLES**

In an isosceles triangle, the angles opposite the congruent sides are congruent. Thus, m∠c = m∠c.

Make these notes in your Tool Kit to the right of the double-lined box.

a) Sketch an equilateral triangle and an isosceles triangle.

b) In the equilateral triangle use the same color to shade the interiors of the three equal angles.

c) In the isosceles triangle shade the interiors of the two angles that have the same measure with one color and the interior of the other angle with a different color.

MC-87.   Find the value of each variable in the following triangles.  The triangles in parts (a) and (b) are equilateral.

a)

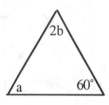

b)

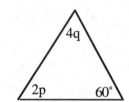

c)

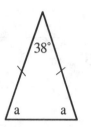

d)

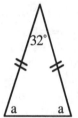

e)

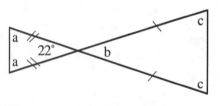

f)

MC-88.   John Edward multiplied (8)(17) in three different ways.  Find the value of each of these expressions.

a)   8(12) + 8(5)          b)   8(10) + 8(7)          c)   8(8) + 8(9)

d)   What do you notice about the value of these expressions?

MC-89.   Each of the diagrams below matches one of the expressions in the previous problem.  Sketch each diagram and write the corresponding expression next to the appropriate diagram.

a)

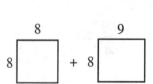

b)

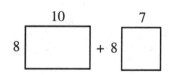

c)

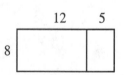

d)   Where is the 17 "hiding" in parts (a) through (c)?  Make up one more problem based on these patterns.

MC-90. Use complete sentences to describe the relationship between the diagram and its expression in the problem above.

MC-91. Draw at least two different diagrams to illustrate the product 5 · 19.

MC-92. Frieda and Gertrude were working on their homework together when Frieda noticed that Gertrude had a different diagram for 5(19) on her paper. Gertrude's diagram is shown at right.

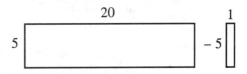

a) What is different about Gertrude's diagram compared with the answers in problem MC-89?

b) Does Gertrude's diagram give the same answer as your diagrams for the previous problem? Explain.

c) Does the same relationship work with subtraction? Explain.

MC-93.

---

**DISTRIBUTIVE PROPERTY**

The **DISTRIBUTIVE PROPERTY** allows us to separate or group quantities in multiplication problems. We can represent the Distributive Property symbolically, numerically, and pictorially.

Symbolically:

$a(b + c) = ab + ac$

Numerically:

$8(10 + 5) = 8(10) + 8(5)$
$\qquad\ = 80 + 40$
$\qquad\ = 120$

Pictorially

---

Make these notes in your Tool Kit to the right of the double-lined box.

Use the example at right to show how a standard multiplication problem is an application of the Distributive Property 7(6) and 7(20).

26
X 7

MC-94. Calculate each of the products below. Use the Distributive Property to show your subproblems.

Example: 8 · 74 = 8(70 + 4) = 8(70) + 8(4) = 592.

a)    9 · 84          b)    15 · 22          c)    5 · 99

MC-95.   A group leaves Mars Station Gamma to climb Olympus
         Mountain. After climbing two miles, 12 people drop
         out, exhausted from the trek. Half a mile later, a
         Martian Jetcopter brings in six more hikers. An hour
         later, four more people drop out. The Jetcopter that
         picks them up brings in five more people. When they
         make it to the summit, the group has 39 people. How
         many people started the trip?

MC-96.   Complete the following Diamond Problems.

Product

Sum

a)    b)    c)    d) 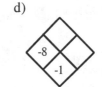   e)

a) $-4$, $3$
b) $-21$, $7$
c) $-108$, $9$
d) $-8$, $-1$
e) $72$, $6$

MC-97.   Use 2, 7, 4, and 3 to write an equation that equals 12. The numbers may be arranged in
         any order, but the order of operations must be observed.

MC-98.   **Algebra Puzzles**  Solve the following equations for x. First collect like terms and show
         all your work.

a)   $3x - 7 + 2x = 23$          b)   $8x + 14 - 7x = 2$

c)   $27 = 7x - 2 - 5x + 7$      d)   $17 - 8x + 4x - 10 = 3$

MC-99.   Andrea and Alexis are twins. They have a brother
         who is eleven years older than they are and a brother
         who is four years younger. The sum of the ages of
         all four children is 35. Write an equation to find the
         sisters' age.

MC-100.  Write and solve a proportion to answer the following
         question.

         Lizzie wants to buy a pair of $112 shoes that are on sale for 30% off. How much will she
         save?

MC-101. Simplify each expression.

a) $\frac{3}{4} \cdot \frac{8}{21}$    b) $\frac{2}{3} + \frac{9}{14}$    c) $\frac{3}{5} \div \frac{1}{2}$    d) $1\frac{3}{4} + 2\frac{2}{5}$

MC-102. Find the largest three-digit number that has only 2 and 5 as prime factors.

MC-103. Follow your teacher's directions for practicing mental math.

MC-104. The diagram below shows a rectangle with two diagonals. We only need to know a few facts in order to find many more.

a) Fact 1: $\overline{AE}$ and $\overline{CE}$ have equal lengths. What kind of triangle is $\triangle AEC$?

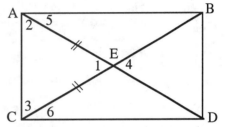

b) What do you know about m∠2 and m∠3?

c) Fact 2: m∠1 = 80°. What is m∠2? m∠3?

d) What do you know about the four corner angles?

e) What do you know about m∠3 and m∠6?

f) What is m∠6? m∠5?

g) If ∠1 can also be named ∠AEC or ∠CEA what are two names for ∠4?

h) What is m∠CED?

MC-105. The fourth grade teacher, Mr. Lopez, gave his class the multiplication problem 13(14). Maria Elena raised her hand almost immediately. "It's 182," she said. Everyone else was still writing.

"How did you get that so quickly?" her teacher asked.

Maria Elena listed her steps.
- First I saw that 14 was 2 times 7.
- Then I multiplied the 2 times the 13 to get 26.
- But 26 is 20 + 6.
- So I multiplied 7 times 20 and 7 times 6.
- And 140 plus 42 is 182.

"Can she do that?" three students asked at once.

"Is her answer correct?" asked Mr. Lopez. All of the students agreed that it was. The class then analyzed the steps she took.

**>>Problem continues on the next page.>>**

| Maria Elena's Steps | Class Analysis |
|---|---|
| First $13(14) = 13(2 \cdot 7)$ | That's okay because $14 = 2 \cdot 7$. |
| Then she grouped the 2 with the 13 and multiplied $13 (2 \cdot 7) \Rightarrow (13 \cdot 2)7 = (26)(7)$ | We call that the Associative Property. You can choose which pair to multiply first. |
| Then she reversed the order $(26)7 = 7(26)$ | The order doesn't change the result. That is called the Commutative Property. |
| She split 26 into $20 + 6$. $7(26) = 7(20 + 6)$ | Clearly $20 + 6$ is just another name for 26. |
| Then she distributed $7(20 + 6) = 7(20) + 7(6)$ | That is the property we are studying now, the Distributive Property. |
| And $7(20) + 7(6) = 140 + 42 = 182$. | She calculated the answer. |

Maria Elena used three basic properties of numbers to make the arithmetic easy enough to do in her head. For each of the following problems, write what was done in each step. State which property (associative, commutative, or distributive) justifies the step for numbers 1 through 9.

a)  $15(29) = 15(30 + (-1))$             (1)

$15(30 - 1) = 15(30) + 15(-1)$       (2)

$150 + (-15) = 150 + (-10 + -5)$      renamed -15 as $-10 + (-5)$

$150 + (-10) + (-5) = (150 + (-10)) + (-5)$    (3)

$140 + (-5) = 135$                Addition

b)  $386 + 177 + 214 = 386 + 214 + 177$     (4)

$386 + 214 + 177 = (386 + 200) + 14 + 177$   (5)

$586 + 14 + 177 = (586 + 14) + 177$      (6)

$600 + 177 = 777$                Addition

c)  $49(12) = 12(49)$                (7)

$12(49) = 12(50 - 1)$           Renamed 49 as $50 - 1$

$12(50 - 1) = 12(50) - 12(1)$        (8)

$12(50) - 12 = (6 \cdot 2)(50) - 12$      Renamed 12 as $6 \cdot 2$

$(6 \cdot 2)(50) - 12 = 6(2 \cdot 50) - 12$      (9)

$6(2 \cdot 50) - 12 = 6(100) - 12$      Renamed $2 \cdot 50$

$600 - 12 = 588$                Subtraction

MC-106.  The Distributive Property allows us to write a problem in two ways: one where you multiply first then add; the other where you add first then multiply. For example: $4(8) + 4(22) = 4(8 + 22)$. One form of the Distributive Property is given in each problem below. On your paper write both forms and then use the one you think is easier to calculate the answer. Underline the form you thought was easier.

a)  $3 \cdot 7 + 3 \cdot 2$

b)  $15(10 + 1)$

c)  $6 \cdot 7 + 6 \cdot 3$

d)  $11(10 + 9)$

e)  $8 \cdot 14 + 8 \cdot 6$

f)  $21(10 + 4)$

MC-107. One-fourth of the vehicles on Mars are hovercrafts. Half of every kind of vehicle on Mars is built on Earth. Jeddie and Xmytl want to know how many of the vehicles are Earth-built hovercraft. Each of them wrote an equation and drew a diagram. Their work is shown below.

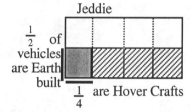

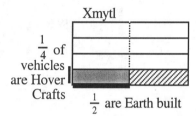

When they looked at each other's work it appeared to them that their results were different. Are the results different or the same? Explain.

MC-108. Next Jeddie showed Xmytl how to add integers using integer tiles. Xmytl liked the integer tiles, but he questioned Jeddie again about what order he should use for adding.

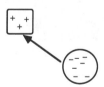

"Look," said Xmytl, "when I add -7 and 3, I start with a field of -7 and put in 3, but when I add 3 and (-7), I start with a field of +3 and put in (-7). That's doing two different things so $3 + (-7)$ must be different from $(-7) + 3$."

Jeddie was puzzled. Explain to him why the order doesn't matter.

MC-109. You can remember the meaning of the word "commutative" from words you already know.

a)  What do "commuters" do every day?

b)  For which of the four arithmetic operations is the Commutative Property true? Show an example for the ones that are not true.

MC-110.

| COMMUTATIVE PROPERTY |

The **COMMUTATIVE PROPERTY** allows us to change the order in which we add or multiply two numbers. We represent the Commutative Property symbolically and numerically as:

<u>Symbolically</u>

$$a + b = b + a \qquad\qquad \text{or} \qquad\qquad a \cdot b = b \cdot a$$
$$\text{(addition)} \qquad\qquad\qquad\qquad\qquad \text{(multiplication)}$$

<u>Numerically</u>

$$-7 + 13 = 13 + (-7) \qquad \text{or} \qquad (-4) \cdot 17 = 17 \cdot (-4)$$
$$6 = 6 \qquad\qquad\qquad\qquad\qquad -68 = -68$$

## ASSOCIATIVE PROPERTY

The **ASSOCIATIVE PROPERTY** allows us to regroup in an addition problem with three terms or a multiplication problem with three factors. We represent the Associative Property symbolically and numerically as:

<u>Symbolically</u>

$$a + (b + c) = (a + b) + c \qquad \text{or} \qquad a \cdot (b \cdot c) = (a \cdot b) \cdot c$$
$$\text{(addition)} \qquad\qquad\qquad\qquad\qquad \text{(multiplication)}$$

<u>Numerically</u>

$$7 + (-7 + 3) = (7 + (-7)) + 3 \qquad \text{or} \qquad 4(-25 \cdot 9) = (4 \cdot (-25)) \cdot 9$$
$$7 + -4 = 0 + 3 \qquad\qquad\qquad\qquad 4(-225) = (-100)(9)$$
$$3 = 3 \qquad\qquad\qquad\qquad\qquad -900 = -900$$

Make these notes in your Tool Kit to the right of the double-lined box.

a)  How will you remember the names for the Commutative, Associative, and Distributive Properties and which rule goes with which name?

b)  Make a note next to your Tool Kit entry that the Commutative Property does <u>not</u> apply to subtraction or division.

MC-111.  Use >, <, or = to compare the following pairs of fractions.

a)  $\dfrac{5}{12}$ —— $\dfrac{4}{9}$    b)  $\dfrac{3}{8}$ —— $\dfrac{5}{12}$    c)  $\dfrac{2}{3}$ —— $\dfrac{3}{5}$

d)  $\dfrac{6}{7}$ —— $\dfrac{5}{6}$    e)  $\dfrac{7}{12}$ —— $\dfrac{6}{11}$    f)  $\dfrac{1}{3}$ —— $\dfrac{3}{10}$

MC-112. Ankit visited Mars Station Alpha, Omega, and Gamma. At each of them he was given 4 baps, 12 zips, and 5 dops to put in his bag.

a) When he got back to base camp, how many of each item did he have in his bag?

b) Simplify this representation of the problem: 3(4B + 12Z + 5D).

MC-113. Janelle was busy keeping records for the colony. She recorded the number of pounds of Mars rocks collected each day: 32, 47, 25, 27, 36, 75, 40, 41, 33, 35, 32, 32, 28, and 75.

a) Make a stem-and-leaf plot to help her organize the information so she can get a better idea of how hard the prospectors are working.

b) Find the mean, median, and mode for the information.

c) Which measure of central tendency was affected by the outlier of 75 pounds?

MC-114. Use the numbers 13, 8, 9, and 0 to write two equations, one for the largest number you can find and one for the smallest number you can find. (Remember that negative numbers are smaller than positive numbers.)

MC-115. Simplify each of the following fractions.

a) $3\frac{1}{3} + 4\frac{7}{8}$

b) $\frac{5}{6} - 1\frac{1}{5}$

c) $2\frac{1}{4} + \frac{5}{6}$

d) $4\frac{1}{4} \div \frac{2}{3}$

MC-116. Solve these percent problems using proportions.

a) If you get 23 out of 30 points on a quiz, what percent did you get?

b) If you want at least 75% on a 60-point quiz, how many points do you need to earn?

c) If your friend got 75% on a quiz and earned 60 points, how many points was the quiz worth?

MC-117. The least common multiple (LCM) of 3, 5, and 6 is:

(A) 90         (B) 30         (C) 33         (D) 60

MC-118. Create a table to organize a set of points which follow the rule $y = \frac{3}{4}x + 2$.
Graph the ordered pairs on a coordinate grid.

MC-119. Compute and compare the answers for each pair of problems.

a)   $10 - 7$ and $7 - 10$

b)   $26 - 15$ and $15 - 26$

c)   $-4 - 6$ and $6 - (-4)$

d)   $-8 - (-15)$ and $-15 - (-8)$

e)   What do you notice about these problems and their answers?

f)   Is subtraction commutative?

MC-120. Xmytl's teacher gave him a bunch of division problems to do. Xmytl hated division. But, he remembered that he had the calculator Jeddie had given him. He used the calculator to do these problems. Here are his solutions

$$9\overline{)45} = 0.2 \qquad\qquad 6\overline{)12} = 0.5 \qquad\qquad 1\overline{)3} = 0.\overline{3}$$

a)   How did he get these answers?

c)   Is division commutative?

d)   How are the answers to $20 \div 5$ and $5 \div 20$ related?

e)   In general, how are the answers $a \div b$ and $b \div a$ related?

MC-121. The **Commutative Property** changes the order of numbers, while the **Associative Property** changes how the numbers are grouped. An example of the Associative Property is $(2 + 3) + 5 = 2 + (3 + 5)$. Simplify the following expressions using the order of operations.

a)   $(-2 + 3) + 6$     b)   $(5 - 8) - 9$     c)   $(3 \cdot 4) \cdot 6$     d)   $(24 \div 12) \div 2$

e)   $-2 + (3 + 6)$     f)   $5 - (8 - 9)$     g)   $3(4 \cdot 6)$     h)   $24 \div (12 \div 2)$

i)   Based on your answers to parts (b) and (f), is the Associative Property true for subtraction?

j)   Based on your answers to parts (d) and (h), is the Associative Property true for division?

k)   For which of the four basic arithmetic operations is the Associative Property true? Show an example for each.

l)   Make a note in your Tool Kit next to the Associative Property that says this property does not apply to subtraction or division.

MC-122.   In addition to the Commutative and Associative Properties, we have used the Identity Property of Multiplication (**Giant 1**) and the Distributive Property. For each problem below, write the problem and the property it demonstrates.

   a)   $12 \cdot 20 = 20 \cdot 12$

   b)   $(98 + 75) + 25 = 98 + (75 + 25)$

   c)   $12 + 19 = 19 + 12$

   d)   $\frac{5}{6} = \frac{10}{12}$

   e)   $4(25 \cdot 9) = (4 \cdot 25) \cdot 9$

   f)   $8(600) + 8(4) = 8(600 + 4)$

   g)   $(12 \cdot 5) \cdot 6 = 12(5 \cdot 6)$

   h)   $\frac{5}{7} = \frac{15}{21}$

   i)   $26 + (38 + 74) = (26 + 38) + 74$

   j)   $8(100 - 1) = 8(100) - 8(1)$


MC-123.   **Martian Supply Central**  This is a partial list of the required supplies <u>per</u> <u>month</u> for each settlement on Mars.

|  | Mars Station Alpha | Mars Station Omega | Mars Station Gamma |
|---|---|---|---|
| Barrels of Water | 12 | 15 | 9 |
| Boxes of Food Bars | 27 | 18 | 15 |
| Cases of Corn Dogs | 12 | 16 | 10 |
| Sleep Sacks | 19 | 19 | 19 |

   Here is an example of how the Distributive Property can help you determine supply requirements for all of the settlements.

   How many barrels of water do you need to meet the needs of all three settlements for the next six months?

$$6(12) + 6(15) + 6(9) = 6(12 + 15 + 9)$$
$$= 6(36)$$
$$= 216$$

   a)   Follow the Distributive Property example for water to show how to find the total number of boxes of food bars you need for all three settlements for the next six months.

   b)   Follow the Distributive Property example for water to show how to find the total number of cases of corn dogs you need for all three settlements for the next <u>year</u>.

   c)   Follow the Distributive Property example for water to find the total number of sleep sacks needed for all three settlements for the next three years.


MC-124.   The space transporter had just arrived with 300 cases of Veggie Squares, a five-month supply. On their monthly order form, Station Alpha ordered 22 cases and Station Gamma ordered 17, but Supply Control had lost Station Omega's monthly order form. Write and solve an equation to figure out how many Veggie Squares Station Gamma's ordered for one month.

MC-125. Quan and Dione were solving the same equation, when Quan looked over and asked, "What are you doing?  You're not working backward."

Quan's Work

$$3(2x - 7) = -51$$
$$2x - 7 = -17$$
$$2x = -10$$
$$x = -5$$

Dione's Work

$$3(2x - 7) = -51$$
$$6x - 21 = -51$$
$$6x = -30$$
$$x = -5$$

Dione said she didn't know what $51 \div 3$ was so she used the Distributive Property and then worked backward to solve.

First use Quan's method to solve each equation below, then use Dione's method.

a)   $6(7 + 10x) = -78$

b)   $10(8x + 9) = 50$

c)   Which method is easier for you?

MC-126.  Use the method you prefer to solve each of these equations.

a)   $5(2x - 7) = -65$

b)   $12(5 - x) = 48$

c)   $8(3x + 6) = 36$

d)   $2(6x + 7) = 23$

MC-127.  Anthony is an inspector for the Mars Station Omega Colony Safety Commission.  He needs to inspect the cables that are on the outside of the colony's walls to make sure that the walls are at 90°.  If angles B and A are complementary, then Anthony can be sure that m $\angle$ C is 90°.  Explain why.

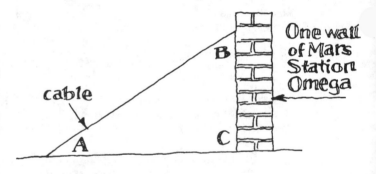

MC-128.  **Algebra Puzzles**  Solve each equation for x.

a)   $2(2x - 3) = -42$

b)   $5(7x + 11) = -50$

c)   $\frac{1}{5}(x - 15) = 7$

d)   $7(2x - 1) + 9 = 30$

MC-129.  The perimeter of an isosceles triangle is 122 centimeters and the base length is 8 more than the two sides that are equal. Draw a diagram, label the sides and write an equation to find the lengths of the sides.

MC-130.  Debbie cut a 60-inch long rope into two unequal pieces. The longer piece is four inches longer than the shorter one. Draw a diagram, label the two pieces, and write an equation. How long is each piece?

MC-131.  Kristie and her two friends, Paige and Sally, were discussing the fact that they would all turn thirteen the next August. Paige was excited because it would be the same day that her grandmother turned 75. Kristie pointed out that Paige was exactly 10 days younger than she was and that Sally was exactly 20 days younger. She said, "If you add up the days of the month we were born you get 45." Use a Guess and Check table or an equation to find out each girl's birthday.

MC-132.  Answer these questions using the flow diagram shown below.

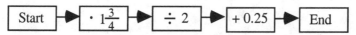

a)  If you start with 8, with what number do you end?

b)  If you start with -12, with what number do you end?

c)  If you start with $\frac{1}{2}$, with what number do you end?

d)  If you end with 1.25, with what fraction did you start?

e)  If you end with $\frac{13}{24}$, with what fraction did you start?

MC-133.  You know that the sum of the angles of a triangle is 180°. If the measures of the angles at A, B, C, D, and E are 36°, find m∠x and m∠y. Assume the star is symmetrical

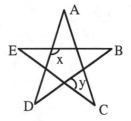

MC-134. In order to become Mars Colony citizens your team must pass the Angles of the Flag test. The angles are labeled in the flag below. Your goal is to use what you know about geometric figures and solving equations to find the measures of all the angles in the flag.

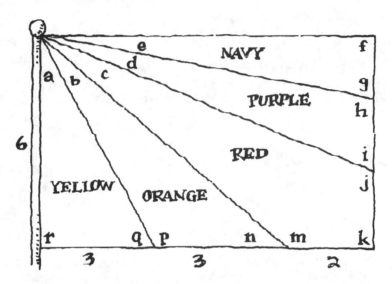

Make a list of the 16 angles. The challenge for your team is to figure out the measures of all 16 angles in the flag based on the clues you get.

a) Clue 1: Three of the angles should be easy to identify because the flag is a rectangle.

b) Clue 2: Look at the sides of the triangle formed by the yellow and orange triangles together. Use that information to find m∠n.

c) What is m∠a + m∠b?

d) Clue 3: m∠a = m∠b + 8° Use this information with your answer to part (c) to write an equation. Now what other angles do you know?

e) Clue 4: What is m∠c + m∠d + m∠e?

f) Clue 5: m∠d + m∠e = m∠c + 3°. Use this clue to write an equation and find m∠c. Now what other angles do you know?

g) Clue 6: m∠e = m∠d + 1°

MC-135. The engineer of the Mars colony needs to replace some rusting pipe with new plastic pipe. He sends his helper, Giovanni, to get one-half of the pipe. His second helper, Mike, is sent to get one-fourth of the pipe. His third helper, Daniela, brings 5 meters of the pipe. Finally, his fourth helper, Barbara, gets the remaining 2 meters. Find the original length of the rusting pipe that is being replaced. You may choose to work backwards, draw a diagram, or write an equation to solve this problem.

MC-136. Write and solve a proportion to answer the following question.

Georgina has a craving for chocolate. She has decided to allow herself to eat one pound of chocolate per week. If she still eats 22 pounds of food per week, what percent of her food is chocolate?

MC-137. **Algebra Puzzles** Solve the following equations. Be sure to collect like terms first.

a) $5.4x + 3.7 + 8.6x + 10.3 = 0$

b) $1 - 14x - 10x - 8 = -5$

c) $16 - p + 5p = 5$

d) $3(6 - 3m) + 5(2m + 7) = 0$

MC-138. Simplify each of the following fractions.

a) $2\frac{11}{12} + \frac{3}{4}$

b) $\frac{3}{4} \cdot 2\frac{1}{3}$

c) $\frac{9}{10} - \frac{1}{2}$

d) $1\frac{3}{4} \div \frac{1}{2}$

MC-139. Complete the following Diamond Problems.

Product

Sum

a)

15   0.5

b)

420

10

c)

-49

7

d)

28

$28\frac{3}{4}$

MC-140. Using a Guess and Check table is one way to solve the problem below. You also may use x for the first number and x + 2 for the second number and use these expressions to write an equation. Solve the problem and then write your answer in a complete sentence.

Find two consecutive odd numbers whose sum is 276.

MC-141. Use a Guess and Check table or write an equation to solve the problem below. Write your answer in a complete sentence.

Dina received a shipment of 34 bins of skin saver. She knew that Mars Station Gamma was supposed to receive twice as many bins as Mars Station Omega, and Mars Station Alpha should have two more bins than Mars Station Omega. How many bins of skin saver should she send to each settlement?

MC-142. Mrs. Baker has a collection of pet slugs. Last week the mode amount of slime they produced was 12 pounds. The median amount of slime they produced was 14 pounds. The mean amount of slime they produced was 18 pounds. Create a list of seven numbers that would create the statistics she is reporting.

MC-143. **Chapter Summary** In this chapter we have studied some properties of numbers and some geometric properties.

- **Properties of Numbers:** The Associative, Commutative, Distributive, and Identity Properties can make calculations easier.

- **Geometric Properties:** Complementary, supplementary, and vertical angles help solve angle problems. Properties of equilateral and isosceles triangles and the sums of angles in triangles and quadrilaterals are also useful.

With your team make a poster that lists each property with an example.

MC-144. This rectangular flag is composed of a gold equilateral triangle, two trapezoidal blue stripes on the borders, and a red stripe between them. Find the measure of each angle labeled with a variable.

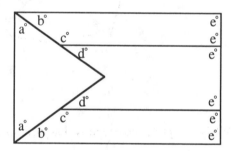

MC-145. You are given two angles in the figure at right. Copy the diagram on your paper and fill in the measures of the other angles.

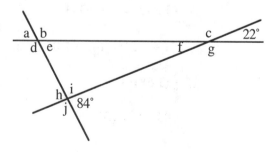

MC-146. Use your knowledge of geometry to write an equation for each of the problems below. Solve your equations to find the lengths of the sides or the measures of the angles.

a)

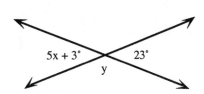

b)

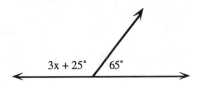

c)

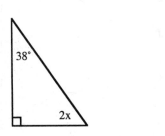

d)    This triangle is isosceles.

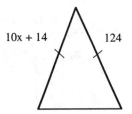

e)

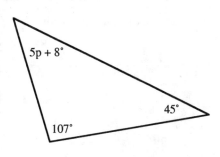

f)    This triangle is isosceles.

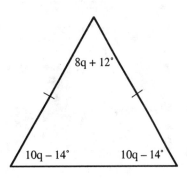

MC-147. Write the property that justifies each equation below.

a)  $(-3)(8 + 12) = (-3)(8) + (-3)(12)$

b)  $-26 + (28 + 42) = (-26 + 28) + 42$

c)  $193(77) = 77(193)$

d)  $\frac{4}{5} = \frac{-32}{-40}$

e)  $83 + (-64) = (-64) + 83$

f)  $6(17 \cdot 10) = (6 \cdot 17)(10)$

g)  $\frac{5}{8}(1.6) = 1$

h)  $47 + (-47) = 0$

i)  $103 + 0 = 103$

MC-148. Tim is thinking of a number. If he subtracts 7, adds 5, and then divides by 3, the result is 9.

     a) Write an equation to represent Tim's number puzzle.

     b) Solve your equation to find his number.

     c) Check your result.

MC-149. Here is a graphical look at proportions and percents. Copy and complete the table below.

| Picture | Problem in Words / Proportion | Answer |
|---|---|---|
| Sketch the picture and fill in the missing parts.<br>250 ⌐ 100%<br><br>n ▮ 38%<br>0 ▮ 0% | What is 38% of 250?<br><br>—— = —— | |
| 69.44 ⌐ n%<br>62 ▮ 100%<br><br>0 ▮ 0% | State the question in words.<br><br>—— = —— | |

MC-150. **Algebra Puzzles** Solve these equations.

     a) $10(4.7x + 8.2) = -12$          b) $\frac{1}{3}(c - 8) = 12$

     c) $100(3m + 2) + m + 4 = 1709$     d) $5k - 4\frac{3}{4}k + 25 = 426$

MC-151.  **What We Have Done in This Chapter**

Below is a list of the Tool Kit entries from this chapter.

- MC-2      Types of Angles
- MC-22    Properties of Angle Pairs
- MC-25    Naming Angles
- MC-53    Angles in a Triangle
- MC-57    Angles in a Quadrilateral
- MC-68    Classifying Triangles by Side Length
- MC-73    Guidelines for Combining Like Terms
- MC-86    Angles in Equilateral and Isosceles Triangles
- MC-93    Distributive Property
- MC-110  Commutative and Associative Properties

Review all the entries and read the notes you made in your Tool Kit. Make a list of any questions, terms, or notes you do not understand. Ask your partner or study team members for help. If anything is still unclear, ask your teacher.

Chapter 9

# Chapter 9
## *Zappo Cola Containers:* **CIRCLES AND CYLINDERS**

A circumference walk will help you develop an understanding of the diameter, radius, and circumference of circles. We will also explore the relationship between the radius and area of circles. Further investigation will develop the formula for volume and surface area of prisms and cylinders. The knowledge and experience you gain in this chapter will help you design and build new soda cans for the "Zappo Soda Corporation" and solve complicated problems involving the area, volume, and surface area of various geometric shapes.

In this chapter you will have the opportunity to:

- develop an understanding of the vocabulary of circles and polygons.

- explore the circumference and area of circles.

- develop and use the formulas for finding the volume and surface area of prisms and cylinders.

- continue working with fractions and decimals.

- practice more coordinate graphing.

- improve your ability to solve equations and use subproblems to solve complex problems.

Read the following problem carefully, **but do not try to solve it now**. What you learn over the next few days will enable you to solve it.

ZC-0.  Zappo Sodas wants to introduce a new soda, Cola Pi-Mega. The can for this new soda will be impressive. In fact, it will hold 1000 cubic centimeters (1 liter) of soda. The designers want the height to be 20 centimeters. They will need to determine the area of the base and build a model of the new can.

| | | |
|---|---|---|
| Number Sense | | |
| Algebra and Functions | | |
| Mathematical Reasoning | | |
| Measurement and Geometry | | |
| Statistics, Data Analysis, & Probability | | |

# Chapter 9
## Zappo Cola Containers: CIRCLES AND CYLINDERS

ZC-1.

---

### CIRCLE

A **CIRCLE** is the set of all points that are the same distance from a fixed point, G. We use ⊙ **G** as the **symbol to represent a circle**, in this case circle G, where G is the center. The fixed point is called the **CENTER** of the circle and the distance from the center to the points on the circle is called the **RADIUS** (usually denoted r). A line segment drawn through the center of the circle with both endpoints on the circle is called a **DIAMETER** (denoted d). Note: d = 2r.

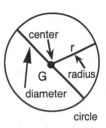

You can think of a circle as the rim of a bicycle wheel. The center of the circle is the hub where the wheel is bolted to the bicycle's frame. The radius is a spoke of the wheel.

---

Highlight these words in your Tool Kit: "circle," "rim," "center," "hub," "radius," "spoke."

ZC-2.    This activity will take place outside. You will need to get a resource page from your teacher on which to make predictions and record your observations. Pay careful attention to the top row of numbers given to you and the actual steps (heel to toe) your classmates take around the circle. Complete the table and graph the results on the resource page.

a)    Complete this table during the activity.

| Radius heel-toes | | | | | |
|---|---|---|---|---|---|
| Diameter heel-toes | | | | | |
| Actual Circumference heel-toes | | | | | |

b)    Graph the diameter and circumference on the grid below.

c)    Describe the relationship between the diameter (d) and the circumference (C).

d)    Describe how to estimate the circumference of a circle based on the diameter. Do not write a formula.

e)    If a student walked a radius of 8 heel-toes, use your graph to estimate the number of heel-toes it would take that person to walk the circumference.

f)    If a student walked a circumference of about 18 heel-toes, approximately how many heel-toes did that person walk for the radius?

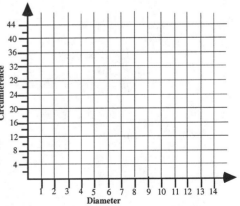

ZC-3.    For each of the circles drawn below, estimate the circumference.

a)

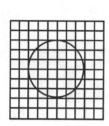

b)

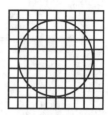

c)

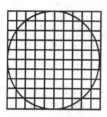

d)

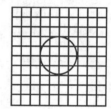

ZC-4.    Solve for the variables.

a)

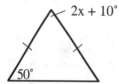

b)

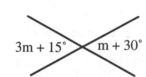

c)

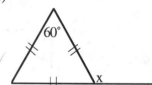

ZC-5.    Answer these questions using the flow diagram shown below.

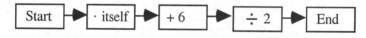

a)    If you start with 5, with what number do you end?

b)    If you start with -9, with what number do you end?

c)    If you start with 10, with what number do you end?

d)    If you <u>end</u> with 35, with what number did you start?

e)    If you <u>end</u> with 63.5, with what number did you start?

CHAPTER 9

ZC-6. Simplify.

a) $1\frac{5}{6} + \frac{9}{10}$

b) $\frac{4}{5} - \frac{3}{7}$

c) $3\frac{1}{3} \cdot \frac{4}{5}$

d) $\frac{1}{7} \div \frac{1}{4}$

ZC-7. On a coordinate grid, plot the following points:

A (2, -1)    B (6, -1)    C (6, 1)    D (4, 2)    E (2, 2)

a) Connect the points in order, from A to B to C to D to E and back to A.

b) Plot the point (2, 1) and connect it to point (6, 1).

c) Connect the points (4, 2) and (4, 1).

d) Compute the area of the three regions inside figure ABCDE.

ZC-8. Find the area and perimeter of the following figures.

a)

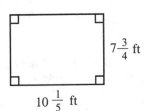

$7\frac{3}{4}$ ft

$10\frac{1}{5}$ ft

b)

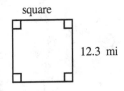

square

12.3 mi

c)

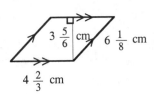

$3\frac{5}{6}$ cm     $6\frac{1}{8}$ cm

$4\frac{2}{3}$ cm

d)

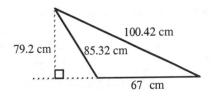

100.42 cm

79.2 cm     85.32 cm

67 cm

ZC-9. Now that we have started a new chapter, it is time for you to organize your binder.

a) Put the work from the last chapter in order and keep it in a separate folder.

b) When this is completed, write "I have organized my binder."

ZC-10.    Obtain the resource page from your teacher with a large circle on it or make a large circle on a sheet of paper by tracing the outline of a circular object like a plate.

a)    Draw a diameter on your circle.

b)    Stretch a piece of string across the diameter and cut the string to that length. Cut another two pieces of string with exactly the same length.

c)    Tape your first piece of string along the circumference of your circle. Estimate the fraction of the circumference you have covered with the diameter. Write down your estimate below the circle.

d)    Tape another piece of string along the circumference, starting at the end of your first string. Estimate the fraction of the circumference you have covered with the two diameters.

e)    Place and tape the third piece of string along the circumference. Connect it to either of the other two pieces. Is there a gap left over? Will another diameter fit in the gap?

f)    In complete sentences, explain how many diameters are in a circumference.

ZC-11.

Pi (π) is the name of the number that is the ratio $\frac{\text{circumference}}{\text{diameter}}$ for any circle. Because its value is not an exact integer or fraction, you must use an approximation when you calculate with it. There are several different approximations you can use for π depending on how accurate you need to be.

You need to consider the purpose of your calculation when you choose which approximation to use.

**>>Problem continues on the next page.>>**

## CIRCUMFERENCE OF CIRCLES

The **CIRCUMFERENCE** of a circle is the perimeter of the circle, that is, the distance around the circle.

To find the circumference of a circle using its diameter, use: $C = \pi \cdot d$.

To find the circumference of a circle using its radius, use: $C = 2\pi \cdot r$.

### FORMS OF $\pi$

| Type of Situation | Form of $\pi$ to Use |
|---|---|
| rough estimation or mental calculation | 3 |
| approximate fraction | $3\frac{1}{7}$ or $\frac{22}{7}$ |
| scientific calculation | $\boxed{\pi}$ (on calculator) or 3.141592654 |
| decimal to the nearest hundredth | 3.14 |

Answer the following questions to the right of the double-lined box in your Tool Kit.

a) If you know the radius of a circle, what will you do to find the circumference?

b) If you know the circumference of a circle, what will you do to find the diameter?

ZC-12. Copy and complete the table below. Use the appropriate form of $\pi$ given in problem ZC-11. Round all circumference answers to the nearest tenth unless you give a fraction answer.

a)

6 m

O

b)

$4\frac{1}{4}$ in

O

c)

1.5 cm

O

| | Circumference of Circle (a) | Circumference of Circle (b) | Circumference of Circle (c) |
|---|---|---|---|
| Rough Estimate | | | |
| Fraction Calculation | | | |
| Scientific Calculation | | | |

ZC-13.  Find the circumference of the following circles. Round all circumference answers to the nearest tenth unless you give a fraction answer.

a)   A circle with a diameter of 16 inches.

b)   A circle with a radius of 3.5 centimeters.

c)   A circle with a perimeter of 56 meters.

ZC-14.   A clock has a minute hand that is 11 inches long. How many inches does the tip of the minute hand travel in:

a)   60 minutes?          b)   15 minutes?          c)   75 minutes?

ZC-15.  Convert each fraction to a decimal.

a)   $\frac{2}{8}$          b)   $\frac{3}{2}$          c)   $\frac{4}{3}$

d)   $\frac{25}{8}$          e)   $\frac{15}{45}$          f)   $\frac{37}{6}$

ZC-16.   **Algebra Puzzles**   Solve each equation.

a)   $2(m - 3) = -2$          b)   $4(2x + 5) - 15 = 29$

c)   $8.5x + 2 - 8x = 13$          d)   $\frac{4}{3}y - 10 = 6$

ZC-17.   The boys in Mrs. Nguyen's class were trying to solve a probability problem about coins. They believe that if they flip one coin the chances of getting heads will be 50%, because there are two sides on a coin, only one of which is heads. If they flip two coins, what is the probability that both coins will come up heads? Draw a picture or list all the possible outcomes help you to answer this question.

ZC-18.    At right is a graph of seven coordinate points.

a)    Write the coordinates of the points in a table
and organize them.

| x | -3 | -2 | -1 | 0 | 1 | 2 | 3 |
|---|---|---|---|---|---|---|---|
| y | | 0.5 | | | | | |

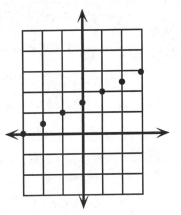

b)    What algebraic rule created these points?

c)    Name at least two other points that would fit
this rule.

ZC-19.    Solve for the variables.

a)

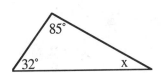

b)

c)

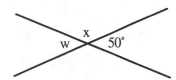

ZC-20.    Obtain a resource page from your teacher.

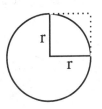

a)    Use a colored pencil to draw the radius twice at right angles (as
shown) and label them r.  Complete a square by drawing the
last two sides (shown with dashed lines) the same length as the
radius.

b)    Shade the square you just drew.  We call this a radius square.

c)    Write an expression to represent the area of this square.

d)    Draw three more radius squares as you did in parts (a) through (c) to cover the
entire circle.  What is the total area of the squares?

e)    Is the area of the circle greater or less than the area of the four radius squares?

ZC-21.    Use the other circle on your resource page.

a)    Use a colored pencil to draw two diameters at right angles as shown. Connect the endpoints to form four radius triangles.

b)    Shade the radius triangles.

c)    What is the area of each of the triangles in the drawing? What is the area of all four radius triangles together?

d)    How many radius squares are the four radius triangles equivalent to?

e)    Is the area of the circle greater or less than the area of the radius triangles, $2r^2$?

ZC-22.    The area of the circle is greater than the area of two radius squares, $2r^2$, but it is smaller than the area of four radius squares, $4r^2$. About how many radius squares do you think cover the area of the circle? Write complete sentences to explain your answer.

ZC-23.    Use the steps below to find a formula for the area of a circle.

a)    Draw four identical circles on construction paper. The size does not matter, but a radius of at least 5 cm is recommended.

b)    Divide the first circle into four identical pieces, with each central angle measuring exactly 90°.

c)    Cut these pieces out and arrange them on your paper as shown in the figure at right. (The picture is not drawn to scale.)

Notice that the figure looks a little like a bumpy parallelogram.

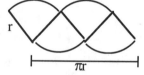

d)    Label the straight edge of the "parallelogram" with r because it is the radius. Label the bumpy edge with
        $\pi r$ because it is almost the same length as half the circumference.

e)    Divide the second circle into eight identical parts, with each central angle measuring exactly 45°. Repeat steps (c) and (d).

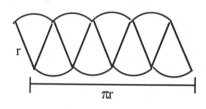

CHAPTER 9

ZC-24.  If you had time, you could
cut the third circle into
sixteen identical parts, with
each central angle measuring
exactly 22.5°.  Pasting them
together would make a
smoother parallelogram then
the first two.  Imagine
cutting the circle into many,

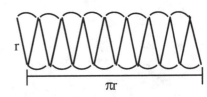

many parts and taping them together to make a figure as you did in problem ZC-23.  The
figure would look almost exactly like a rectangle with base πr and height r.

a)  What would be the area of the rectangle?

b)  Explain how this is related to the area of
the original circle.

c)  Write the formula for the area of a circle.

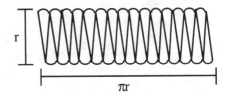

ZC-25.

```
┌─────────────────────────────────────────────────────────────┐
│                     AREA OF CIRCLES                           │
│                                                               │
│  The AREA of a circle is the measure of the region inside it. │
│  To find the area of a circle when given the radius, use this │
│  formula:                                                     │
│                                                               │
│                 A = π · r · r = πr²                           │
│                                                               │
└─────────────────────────────────────────────────────────────┘
```

**AREA OF CIRCLES**

The **AREA** of a circle is the measure of the region inside it.  To find the area of a
circle when given the **radius**, use this formula:

$$A = \pi \cdot r \cdot r = \pi r^2$$

In your Tool Kit create an example to show how to calculate the area of a circle when you
know its radius.

ZC-26.  Find the circumference and area of a circle with:

a)  r = 8 inches        b)  d = 22 cm            c)  r = 5.7 cm

ZC-27.   Kathleen is wrapping a candle to give to a friend. Which is the best piece of wrapping paper (A, B, or C) for her use?  Explain your answer.

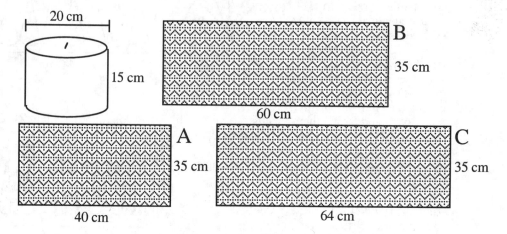

ZC-28.   Simplify.

a)  $\frac{3}{8} + \frac{4}{12}$

b)  $2\frac{1}{2} - 1\frac{3}{4}$

c)  $\frac{8}{9} \cdot 2\frac{1}{2}$

d)  $15 \div \frac{3}{4}$

ZC-29.   Pham keeps track of the blood supply in his area.  Every month he fills out a report that states how much above or below a minimum number of units of blood is contained in storage.  A negative number indicates a shortage of blood and a positive number indicates a surplus.  The table below summarizes the blood supply for the last twelve months.

| Month | 1 | 2 | 3 | 4 | 5 | 6 | 7 | 8 | 9 | 10 | 11 | 12 |
|---|---|---|---|---|---|---|---|---|---|---|---|---|
| Blood Supply | -15 | -20 | -10 | 7 | 25 | 30 | -5 | -10 | -20 | -15 | -5 | -10 |

a)   What is the range?

b)   What does this range represent?

c)   Calculate the mean.

d)   Calculate the median.

e)   Calculate the mode.

f)   Which measure of central tendency best describes the data?  Explain your answer.

ZC-30.   Follow your teacher's directions for practicing mental math.

ZC-31.  A circle has a circumference of 32 inches.

   a)   Estimate its diameter to the nearest inch.

   b)   Compute its radius to the nearest inch.

   c)   Compute its area.


ZC-32. Whole pizzas are sold by the size of their diameters. For example, a 12-inch pizza has a diameter of 12 inches.

Dan the Pizza Man told a customer that a 12" medium pizza is $10 and an 18" large pizza is $16. Which pizza is the better deal for the customer (that is, which one costs less per square inch)? You may use a calculator, but you must show your work.

ZC-33. Farmer Rottenberg has tethered Zoe, the baby goat, to the center of the long side of a 50- by 60-foot barn. Zoe can graze on the grass as far as the rope will reach. For the different lengths of rope listed in parts (b) through (e), find the area of the grass field on which Zoe can graze. Show all your work.

   a)   As long as the rope is not longer than 30 feet, Zoe's grazing area is what fraction of a whole circle?

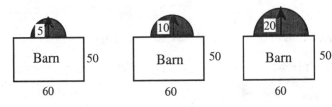

   b)   5 feet                              c)   10 feet

   d)   20 feet                             e)   30 feet

ZC-34.    You are the manager of a carpet warehouse. When you do the annual inventory, you have to find the area of carpet remaining on the rolls. Instead of unrolling the huge rolls and measuring them, workers count the number of layers (complete circumferences) on the roll and use the average diameter to calculate the length. Use the diagram below to help answer the following questions.

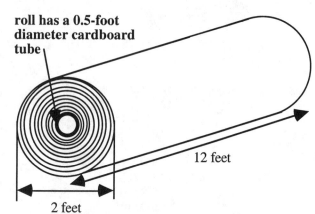

a)    How many complete circumferences are there on this roll? (Count the "rings.")

b)    What is the smallest diameter of a carpet "ring"?

c)    What is the largest diameter of a carpet "ring"?

d)    What is the average diameter of a carpet "ring"? To find it, average the smallest and largest diameters.

e)    Use the average diameter to find the average circumference of a carpet ring.

f)    Use the average circumference and the number of rings to find the approximate length of this roll.

g)    What is the area of the carpet on this roll (in square feet)?


ZC-35.    Find the area for each of the following circles. Use $\pi \approx 3.14$ for parts (a) and (c) and $\frac{22}{7}$ for part (b).

a)    A circle with a radius of 3.4 yards.

b)    A circle with a diameter of $4\frac{2}{3}$ feet.

c)    A circle with a circumference of 628 millimeters.


ZC-36.    Find the area and circumference of the circles below using the radius or diameter. Use the estimation of $\pi$ you prefer.

a)    r = 7.80 meters            b)    d = 13 inches

c)    r = $\frac{7}{11}$ feet            d)    d = 100 miles

ZC-37. In this chapter, you have been studying the circumference of circles.

   a) Create a table to organize a set of points that follow the rule $y = \pi \cdot x$. Use $\pi = \frac{22}{7}$. Graph the ordered pairs on a coordinate grid.

   b) In this graph, what part of the circle do the x-values represent?

   c) In this graph, what part of the circle do the y-values represent?

ZC-38. Which is the larger of the two numbers and by how much?

   a) |-26| and |-19|                    b) |-28| and |-27|

   c) |-3.6| and |3.5|                    d) |-45| and |43|

ZC-39. Many bicycle tires have a diameter of 23 inches.

   a) When a bicycle tire rotates once, how far does the bicycle move forward?

   b) If a bicyclist rides one mile, how many times does the tire rotate? (Remember that 1 mile is 5,280 feet.)

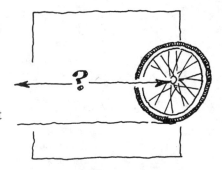

ZC-40. You know the inverse operation for multiplication is division. What is the inverse operation for squaring? That is, how do we unsquare? Find a positive solution for each equation. Round your answer to the nearest tenth.

   a) $r^2 = 25$       b) $r^2 = 100$       c) $r^2 = 30$       d) $r^2 = 45$

ZC-41. In the previous problem, especially parts (c) and (d), did you guess and check or use a key on your calculator? If you did guess and check, see if you can find a key that will unsquare.

ZC-42. The Earth has a circumference of about 25,000 miles.

   a) Use this information to calculate the diameter of the Earth.

   b) If you walked completely around the world, and you are 5 feet tall, how much farther would your head travel than your feet?

ZC-43. The **volume** of a three-dimensional shape is the number of 1 x 1 x 1 cubes needed to build it. For example, the volume of the first figure is 3 cubes. What is the volume of the other shapes below?

Example:    a) 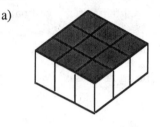    b) 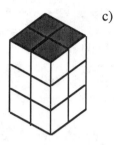    c)

The volume
is 3 cubes.

ZC-44. Obtain a resource page. Cut, fold, and tape the pattern on your resource page to build a solid

a) What is the area of the largest face (base) of your solid?

b) Since the solid is 1 inch thick, what is its volume?

c) Stack all the solids in your team on top of each other. What is the volume of this new solid?

d) If you were to stack all the solids in the classroom that are identical to yours, what would be the volume of this stack?

ZC-45. Get a resource page from your teacher. For each of the figures below:
- Sketch in the 1" x 1" squares that fit on the base.
- Determine how many cubes would be in the layer on the base.
- Determine how many layers would be needed to fill in the figure. Draw in the lines to show the layers.
- Find the volume.

a)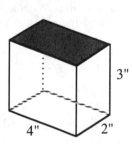

3"
4"    2"

b)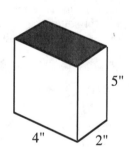

5"
4"    2"

c)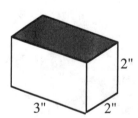

2"
3"    2"

d)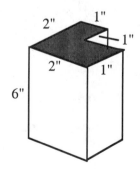

2"    1"
1"
2"    1"
6"

ZC-46. Calculate the area of the base in each of the figures in the previous problem. How does the number of cubes on the bottom layer compare with the area of the base?

ZC-47.

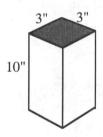

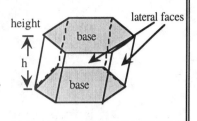

**PRISMS**

A **PRISM** is a three-dimensional figure composed of polygonal faces (called sides or lateral sides) and two congruent, parallel faces called bases. No holes are permitted in the solid. The remaining faces are parallelograms (or rectangles). A prism is named for the shape of its base.

In your Tool Kit on prisms, highlight the sentence that tells how a prism is named.

To the right of the double-lined box in your Tool Kit sketch a prism with a different base.

ZC-48. Which figure in problem ZC-43 is not a prism? Why not?

ZC-49. Find the area of the base of each prism below. Use the idea of layers of cubes on the base to compute the volumes.

a)

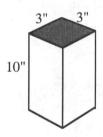

b)

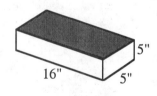

ZC-50. Find the area of the base of each prism below, then use the height to calculate the volume.

a)

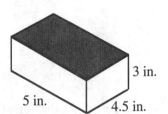

b)

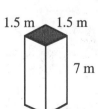

ZC-51.    Write a complete sentence to answer each of the following questions about circles.

    a)    If you know what the radius is, how can you find the diameter?

    b)    If you know what the diameter is, how can you find the radius?

    c)    If you know what the radius is, how can you find the circumference?

    d)    If you know what the diameter is, how can you find the circumference?

    e)    If you know what the radius is, how can you find the area?

    f)    If you know what the diameter is, how can you find the area?

ZC-52.    Add or subtract as indicated.

    a)    $2.3726 - 0.425$             b)    $4.064 + 1.87$

    c)    $1.4752 - 0.632$           d)    $0.004 - 0.00189$

    e)    $45 - 34.73$              f)    $11.057 + 8.873$

    g)    seventeen-tenths plus seventeen plus seventeen-hundredths

ZC-53.    Simplify.

    a)    $\frac{4}{5} + \frac{7}{8}$                 b)    $\frac{7}{8} - \frac{3}{4}$

    c)    $\frac{4}{9} \cdot \frac{6}{10}$               d)    $\frac{2}{3} \div \frac{5}{6}$

ZC-54.    Find the area and perimeter of the following figures.  All measurements are in centimeters.

    a)                                     b)

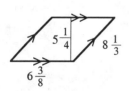
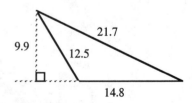

ZC-55.    Dora needs 13 cases of soda for the big end-of-year party for the Math Club.  If three cases of soda cost $21.99, how much will 13 cases of soda cost?

ZC-56. Chrissy has $60.00 to spend on pizza for a party. She can buy 5-inch personal pizzas for $4.95 each or 15-inch pizzas for $29.95. Help her decide which is the better deal.

a) Calculate the area of one 5-inch pizza (to the nearest tenth). Calculate the area of the 15-inch pizza (to the nearest tenth). About how many times bigger is the 15-inch pizza compared to the 5-inch pizza?

b) Which pizza is the better deal? What size pizza should Chrissy buy? How many can she get? Explain.

ZC-57. Solve the problem below using a Guess and Check table. Be sure to write your answer in a complete sentence.

Fred and Ginger want to build a dance floor in their garden. Fred would like a perfectly square dance floor while Ginger prefers a long, narrow floor. Like good partners, they compromise on a floor that is $2\frac{1}{2}$ times as long as it is wide. If the perimeter of the new dance floor is 192.5 ft, find its length, width, and area.

ZC-58.

---

### VOLUME OF A PRISM

The **VOLUME** of a prism is the area of either base (A) times the height (h) of the prism.

$$V = (\text{Area of base}) \cdot (\text{height}) \quad \text{or} \quad V = Ah$$

Example:

Area of base = (2 in.)(3 in.) = 6 in.$^2$

(Area of base)(height) = (6 in.$^2$)(4 in.) = 24 in.$^3$

Volume = 24 in.$^3$

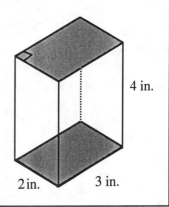

---

Describe how to find the area of the base of a triangular prism in your Tool Kit to the right of the double-lined box.

ZC-59. The formula for the volume of a prism works whether we draw in the cubes or not. Find the area of the base of each prism below and then use the height to calculate the volume.

a)

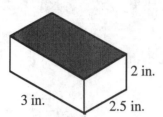

2 in.

3 in.

2.5 in.

b)

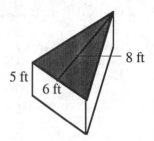

8 ft

5 ft

6 ft

c)

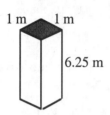

1 m        1 m

6.25 m

ZC-60. Find the volume of each prism. Use the shaded side as the base.

a) Trapezoidal Prism
(base shown below)

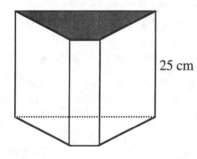

25 cm

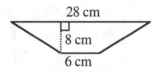

28 cm

8 cm

6 cm

b) Square Prism

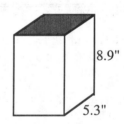

8.9"

5.3"

c) Each edge of the base is 1 cm.

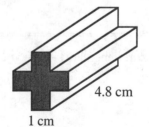

4.8 cm

1 cm

d)

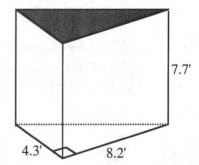

7.7'

4.3'        8.2'

ZC-61. A circle has a circumference of 48 inches. Two radii (remember that "radii" is the plural of the word "radius") from the center cut off $\frac{1}{6}$ of the circle.

    a) What is the length of the part of the circle which was cut off?

    b) The two radii and the $\frac{1}{6}$ part of the circle create a region shaped like a slice of pizza. What is the perimeter of this part?

    c) What is the area of the region described in part (b)?

ZC-62. Use a calculator to solve for a positive solution. Round your answers to the nearest tenth.

    a) $5r = 9$        b) $\pi r = 9$        c) $9r^2 = 45$        d) $\pi r^2 = 45$

ZC-63. If we know the area of a circle, how can we find the radius? the diameter? the circumference? Complete the steps below for a circle with an area of 32 ft$^2$.

    a) What is the formula for the area of a circle?

    b) Therefore: $\pi r^2 = 32$. Why?

    c) The circumference = $2\pi r$ = _____.

ZC-64. Use the same procedure as in problem ZC-63 to find the circumference of a circle with an area of 25 m$^2$.

    a) What is the equation for the area of this circle?

    b) Solve the equation to find the radius.

    c) What is the circumference?

ZC-65. Morgan's pool at right has an area of 400 ft$^2$.

    a) How many feet of fencing are needed to enclose the pool exactly?

    b) If she wants to put a floating circular blanket on the pool to keep it warm, how many square feet of blanket does she need?

400 ft$^2$

ZC-66.    Complete the following Diamond Problems.

Product

Sum

a) 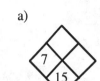   b)    c) 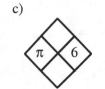   d)    e)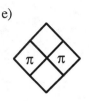

ZC-67.    Answer these questions using the flow diagram below.

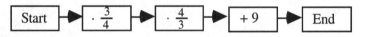

a)    If you start with 5, with what number do you end?

b)    If you start with -9, with what number do you end?

c)    If you start with 10, with what number do you end?

d)    If you end with 35, with what number did you start?

e)    If you start with N, with what number do you end?

f)    Use the word "reciprocal" to describe what is happening in this flow diagram.

ZC-68.    Find each of the following.

a)    $|43| + |-16|$          b)    $|4.1| - |-2.34|$

c)    $|12| + |-2|$           d)    $|-91| - |-6|$

ZC-69.    Here is a graphical look at proportions and percents.  Copy and complete the table.

| Picture | Problem in Words / Proportion | Answer |
|---|---|---|
| n ⌐ 100%<br>168.75  75%<br>0  0% | 168.75 is 75% of what number?<br><br>———— = ———— | |
| 2.5 ⌐ 100%<br>n  30%<br>0  0% | State the question in words.<br><br>———— = ———— | |

ZC-70.    A diagram of the key area of a typical basketball court is shown at right.

a)    List the subproblems you need to solve to find the area of the key and the semi-circle above the free-throw line.

b)    What is the area of the key and semi-circle?

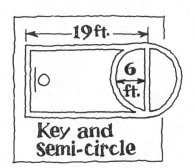

Key and
Semi-circle

ZC-71.    Simplify each expression.

a)    $(9 + 2) \cdot 3 - 6 + 3 \cdot 9$

b)    $16 + 6 \div 3 + (4 - 2)(5)$

c)    $3(4 + 5) - 12 \cdot 2$

d)    $25 + 2 \cdot 3 - 12 \div 4$

ZC-72.   In previous problems we found that a prism of height  h  with base of area  A  has
volume  V = Ah.  This was true for all of the prisms we looked at and is, in fact, true
for any prism.  The same formula also holds for any circular cylinder; that is, if you
have a cylinder of height  h  and its base is a circle of area  A,  then it has volume
V = Ah.

---

**VOLUME OF A CYLINDER**

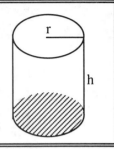

The volume of a cylinder is the area of its base multiplied by its
height:  $V = A \cdot h$.

Since the base of a cylinder is a circle of area $A = \pi r^2$, we can
write:  $V = \pi r^2 h$.

---

In your Tool Kit to the right of the double-lined box, write an example of your own to
show the steps taken to calculate the volume of a cylinder when you know the radius of
the base and the height.

ZC-73.   Find the volume of cylinders with the following measurements.

   a)   r = 4 inches,     b)   r = 8 cm,        c)   r = 3.75 feet,     d)   d = 6 meters,
        h = 5 inches           h = 10 cm             h = 8.5 feet            h = 3 meters

ZC-74.   Find the volume of a soda can with a radius of 5 centimeters and a height of 18
centimeters.  Make a sketch and show your work.

ZC-75.   Farmer Fred has a water storage tank which is a circular cylinder with a diameter of 6 feet
and a height of 10 feet.  It is lying on its side.

   a)   Find the volume of the tank.

   b)   The tank is half full of water so you could calculate its volume by dividing your
        answer for part (a) by 2, but you can also think of the water as part of a cylinder.
        What is the shape of the base of the half filled cylinder?

   c)   Compute the volume of the water using the base shape from part (b).

ZC-76.    Find the area of each shaded **sector** in the circles below.

a)

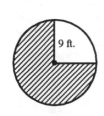
9 ft.

b)

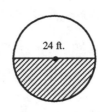
24 ft.

c)

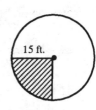
15 ft.

d)

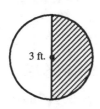
3 ft.

e)

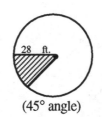
28   ft.

(45° angle)

f)

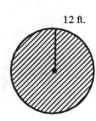
12 ft.


ZC-77.    Find the volumes of these cylinders.

a)    90° cut out, r = 8'

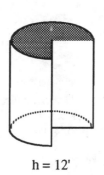

h = 12'

b)    $\frac{1}{3}$ cut out, r = 6 cm

h = 14 cm


ZC-78.    Solve for m.

a)

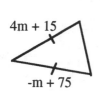
4m + 15

-m + 75

b)

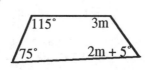
115°    3m

75°    2m + 5°

c)

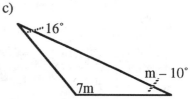
16°

7m

m – 10°


ZC-79.    Suppose a cylinder 4 meters high has a base with an 11" diameter.  Find its volume.

ZC-80. Simplify.

a) $2\frac{3}{5} + 1\frac{9}{12}$

b) $1\frac{4}{9} - \frac{1}{2}$

c) $1\frac{5}{8} \cdot \frac{7}{12}$

d) $\frac{4}{7} \div 1\frac{3}{5}$

ZC-81. Complete the following Diamond Problems.

Product

Sum

a)

b)

c)

d)

e)

ZC-82. Convert each fraction into a decimal.

a) $\frac{17}{34}$

b) $\frac{16}{33}$

c) $\frac{25}{12}$

ZC-83. At right is the top view of a 24-by-24 foot square lawn. There is a sprinkler in the middle of the lawn. Show your work as you solve the following problems.

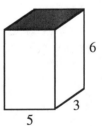

a) What area of the lawn is watered?

b) What area of the lawn is not watered?

c) What percent of the lawn is not watered?

ZC-84. Suppose we have a rectangular prism which has dimensions 5 inches by 3 inches by 6 inches. Its **surface area** is the total area of its six faces.

a) What are the dimensions of the six faces?

b) Find the areas of the six faces.

c) Find the surface area of the prism.

ZC-85.  Find the surface area of the triangular prism
at right. Its base is a right triangle with
sides of length 6 cm, 8 cm, and 10 cm.

The height of the prism is 4 cm.

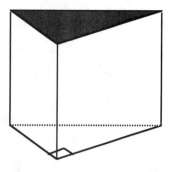

ZC-86.  A **net** is a two-dimensional unfolded picture of a three-dimensional object. Below is a net
for a cylinder. Find the total surface area (the area of the three separate pieces added
together) for the soda can which this net represents.

a)  The height of the soda can is 7.2 cm. The
longer side of the rectangle is the same
measurement as what part of the circle?

b)  Show the subproblems you use to find the
total area (surface area of all three pieces)
of this soda can.

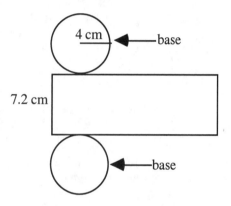

## SURFACE AREA OF PRISMS AND CYLINDERS

The **SURFACE AREA OF A PRISM** is the sum of the areas of all of its faces, including the bases. Surface area is expressed in **square units**.

Example: Find the surface area of the triangular prism at right.

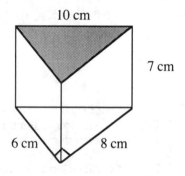

Subproblem 1: Area of the two bases

$$2\left[\tfrac{1}{2}(6 \text{ cm})(8 \text{ cm})\right] = 48 \text{ cm}^2$$

Subproblem 2: Area of the three lateral faces

Area of face 1: $(6 \text{ cm})(7 \text{ cm}) = 42 \text{ cm}^2$
Area of face 2: $(8 \text{ cm})(7 \text{ cm}) = 56 \text{ cm}^2$
Area of face 3: $(10 \text{ cm})(7 \text{ cm}) = 70 \text{ cm}^2$

Subproblem 3: Surface Area of Prism = sum of bases and lateral faces

$$48 \text{ cm}^2 + 42 \text{ cm}^2 + 56 \text{ cm}^2 + 70 \text{ cm}^2 = 216 \text{ cm}^2$$

The **SURFACE AREA OF A CYLINDER** is the sum of the two base areas and the lateral surface area. The formula for the surface area is:

$$\textbf{S.A.} \; = \; \mathbf{2\pi r^2 + \pi dh} \; = \; \mathbf{2\pi r^2 + 2\pi rh}$$

where $r$ = radius, $d$ = diameter, and $h$ = height of the cylinder.

Example: Find the surface area of the cylinder at right.

Subproblem 1: Area of the two circular bases

$2[\pi(28 \text{ cm})^2] = 1568\pi \text{ cm}^2$

Subproblem 2: Area of the lateral face

$\pi(56)25 = 1400\pi \text{ cm}^2$

Subproblem 3: Surface area of the cylinder

$1568\pi \text{ cm}^2 + 1400\pi \text{ cm}^2 = 2968\pi \text{ cm}^2$
$\approx 9324.25 \text{ cm}^2$

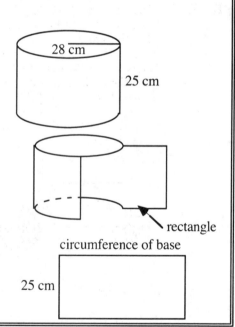

In your Tool Kit below the double-lined box, show and explain the subproblems you would use to find the surface area of the prism in the Tool Kit entry above. Include diagrams of the figures you use in your subproblems.

ZC-88.    The figure at right is a net for a cylinder.

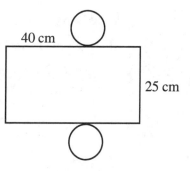

40 cm

25 cm

a)    What is the circumference of the base of this cylinder?  Use this information to solve for the radius of the base.

b)    Find the total surface area of this cylinder.

ZC-89.    Ignacio cut out the net for problem ZC-88.  His younger sister drew a red strip which was 2 cm wide from the bottom left corner to the top right corner.  Find the area of the strip.

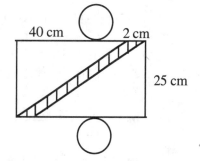

40 cm        2 cm

25 cm

ZC-90.    Mrs. Rottenberg wanted Zoe to have more grass to eat, so she tied Zoe to a corner of the same barn.  This allowed Zoe to graze as before.  Different lengths of rope are listed in parts (b) through (e) below.  Find the area of the grass field Zoe can graze for each of the different rope lengths.  Show all your work.

a)    Zoe's grazing area is what fraction of a whole circle?

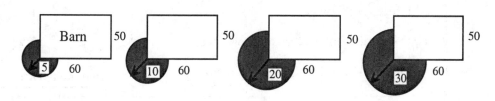

Barn    50        50        50        50

5    60        10    60        20    60        30    60

b)    5 feet                    c)    10 feet

d)    20 feet                   e)    30 feet

ZC-91.    Simplify each expression.

   a)    $18 \div 9 \cdot 9 + 6 \div 2$            b)    $49 - 7 \cdot 2 + 0.3(6 - 4)$

   c)    $56 \div 4 \cdot 7(5 - 6)$               d)    $4 - 6 \cdot 2 + 3(-2)$


ZC-92.    **Algebra Puzzles**  Solve each equation.

   a)    $5w + 15 = -3$                    b)    $6x + 15 = -3$

   c)    $1.5y + 10 = 1$                   d)    $\frac{1}{4}z - 22 = -12$


ZC-93.    Answer the questions below.  Make sure you show your work.

   a)    What is the area of the base of the soda can at right?

   b)    What is the volume of this can?

ZC-94.    Here is a graphical look at proportions and percents.  Copy and complete the table.

| Picture | Problem in Words / Proportion | Answer |
| --- | --- | --- |
| Sketch and shade the picture. Fill in the missing parts. <br> 100% <br> 0 ⌞ 0% | What is 85% of 15? <br><br> ——— = ——— | |
| 7.5 ⌐ 100% <br> 4.575 ⌐ n% <br> 0 ⌞ 0% | State the question in words. <br><br> ——— = ——— | |

ZC-95.    **Zappo Cola (Part 1)**

Zappo Sodas wants to introduce a new soda, Cola Pi-Mega. The can for this new soda will be impressive. In fact, it will hold 1000 cubic centimeters (1 liter) of soda. The designers want the height of the can to be 20 centimeters.

You and your partner are design engineers for Zappo. Complete the following tasks together.

a)    Determine how big the area of the base of the Cola Pi-Mega can has to be.

b)    Find the radius and the circumference of this base. Round your answers to the nearest tenth.

c)    Sketch a net of the Cola Pi-Mega can and label all the dimensions that you know.

d)    Make a model of the Cola Pi-Mega can. Use your sketch to draw an accurate net.

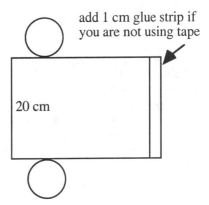

add 1 cm glue strip if you are not using tape

20 cm

ZC-96.    **Zappo Cola (Part 2)**

a)    Use your net from ZC-95 to calculate how many square centimeters of aluminum it takes to make one can. That is, find the surface area of the new can.

b)    The Zappo company plans to manufacture two million cans for test marketing. How many square centimeters of aluminum will be needed for test marketing?

c)    How many six-packs of soda will 2 million cans make?

d)    A standard can of cola is 355 cubic centimeters and weighs 265 grams. If the can of Cola Pi-Mega is proportionately heavier, how much will a Cola Pi-Mega weigh in grams? In kilograms? How much will a six-pack weigh in grams? In kilograms? Is that a reasonable weight for a six-pack since one kilogram is 2.2 pounds?

e)    Zappo Cola has decided to market Cola Pi-Mega in four-packs instead of six-packs. How many pounds will a four-pack weigh? How does this compare to a six-pack of standard soda?

ZC-97. A basketball has a 30-inch circumference, while a basket rim has a 57-inch circumference. What is the distance between the ball and the basket if the ball goes through the center of the rim? (Hint: Find the diameter of each circle first and draw a picture.)

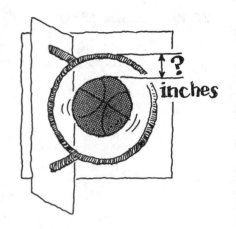

ZC-98.  Which of the cylinders matches the net?

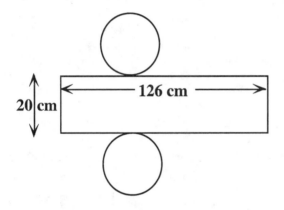

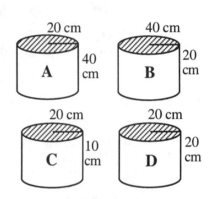

ZC-99. Keiko and Mikabo were trying to figure out how big their model castle would be if they used a scale of 1 inch to 20 feet.

a) If a real castle has dimensions of 500 feet by 800 feet, how large should their castle be? Be sure to find both the length and the width of their model.

b) The girls want to build a circular tower. The real tower has a diameter of 20 feet. What is the circumference of the model tower?

c) They decided to figure out the volume of the original tower which has a diameter of 20 feet and a height of 60 feet. Find the volume of the real tower.

ZC-100.    Find the volume of each of the following prisms.

a)    Cylinder

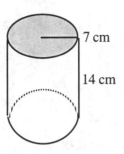

7 cm

14 cm

b)    Rectangular Prism

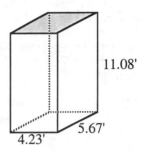

11.08'

5.67'

4.23'

c)    Triangular Prism

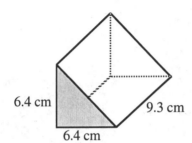

6.4 cm

9.3 cm

6.4 cm

d)    Prism with A = 20 cm$^2$

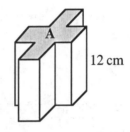

A

12 cm

ZC-101.    Find the area and circumference of the circles below using the radius or diameter given.

a)    d = 25.534 yds        b)    r = 83.589 cm        c)    d = 0.0038 km

ZC-102.    Bobbi was thinking about how many times tires make a complete turn (rotation) when driving down the road. Her car has 13-inch tires, her brother's truck has 14-inch tires, and her dad's mini-van has 15-inch tires. Remember that the distance traveled in one rotation equals the circumference. You also need to know that one mile has 5,280 feet.

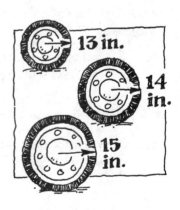

13 in.

14 in.

15 in.

a)    How many inches are in one mile?

b)    How many times will the 13-inch tire turn in one mile?

c)    How many times will the 14-inch tire turn in one mile?

d)    How many times will the 15-inch tire turn in one mile?

ZC-103.   Follow your teacher's directions for practicing mental math.

ZC-104.   Maverick Movie Theater sells
a small tub of popcorn for $1.
To keep their prices proportional,
for how much should they sell
the medium and large tubs?
(The answers are not $2 and $3.)

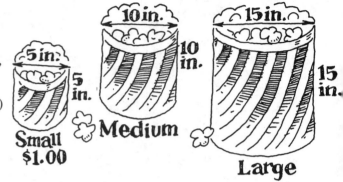

ZC-105.   The diagram at right shows three pizzas.

   a)   What is the area of a small pizza?

   b)   What is the area of a large pizza?

   c)   What area of the large pizza is not
        covered by the two small pizzas?

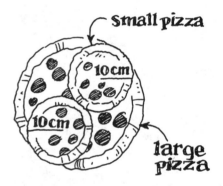

ZC-106.   The diameter of Pizza B is twice as
long as the diameter of Pizza A.

   a)   Calculate the area of each
        pizza.

   b)   Pizza A costs $11.95. Pizza B
        costs $39.95. Which pizza
        should you buy if you want
        the best deal possible?

Pizza A
12"

Pizza B
24"

ZC-107. **Chapter Summary** It is time to summarize and
review what you have learned in this chapter.

a)   List the formulas you used in the Zappo Cola
     Pi-Mega problems ZC-95 and ZC-96.

b)   List the other formulas you have used in this
     chapter.

ZC-108. Mentally estimate the circumference and area of the following circles. Use $\pi \approx 3.0$.

a)   The diameter is $\frac{1}{2}$ inch.

b)   The radius is 6 inches.

c)   The diameter is 8 inches.

d)   The radius is 10 centimeters.

ZC-109. Ann and Nan's math teacher had a popcorn party. Each student made a container for
his/her popcorn by rolling up a piece of paper. Ann's paper is 11 inches by 14 inches.
She made a narrow tube by using the 14-inch side for the height. Nan also used a piece
of paper 11 inches by 14 inches, but she made her tube shorter by using the 11-inch side
for the height. Whose tube holds the most popcorn?

ZC-110. **Algebra Puzzles** Solve each equation.

a)   $2(5x - 12) = -7$

b)   $4(4x + 1) = 0$

c)   $\frac{n - 16}{2} + 7 = -7$

d)   $6(\frac{1}{3} m - 7) = 48$

ZC-111. Bill needed some drip hose for his
orchard. At his local hardware store he
found a bundle with ten loops of hose
advertised as being 100 feet long.

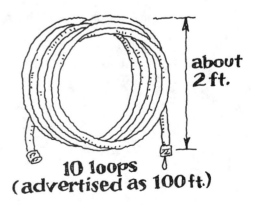

about
2 ft.

10 loops
( advertised as 100 ft.)

a)   If the diameter of the roll is about 2
     feet, is the advertised length correct?

b)   If the diameter of the roll is 3 feet,
     would the store's claim be true?

ZC-112.  Harold Ham is an amateur radio operator in Sacramento, California who is testing his small radio transmitter. Harold's license gives him a legal limit of 150,000 square miles. If he broadcasts outside this area limit, he is subject to a $1,000 fine from the Federal Communication Commission. On several tests he contacted people as far away as Redding using 950 watts of power. Solve the following problems, showing all of your work.

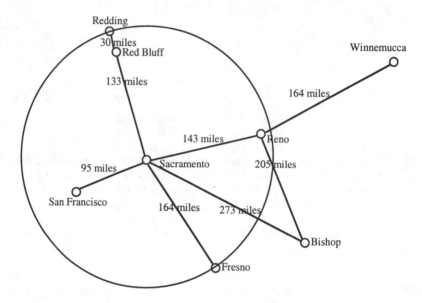

a)  What is the broadcast area in which Harold is operating if he is contacting people only as far as Redding?

b)  If people in Redding are picking up his signal, is he using too much power or is he within his legal broadcast area?

c)  Should Harold lower his signal strength if he hears, "Breaker, breaker... this is Bishop Bob reading you loud and clear from Bishop..."?

d)  Should Harold lower his signal strength if he hears, "This is Reno Ron, reading you loud and clear from Reno..."?

e)  If Harold wants to upgrade his license so he can reach his friend Will in Winnemucca, how much power should he be licensed to use if power is proportional to the area reached be the signal? Set up and solve a proportion. You need to use the fact that Sacramento, Reno, and Winnemucca are almost in a straight line.

f)  If 950 watts of power gives him a 164-mile radius, how much power should he use to get his maximum legal limit of 150,000 square miles of area? Show your subproblems.

ZC-113. **What We Have Done in This Chapter**

Below is a list of the Tool Kit entries from this chapter.

- ZC-1     Circle
- ZC-11    Circumference of Circles
- ZC-25    Area of Circles
- ZC-47    Prisms
- ZC-58    Volume of a Prism
- ZC-72    Volume of a Cylinder
- ZC-87    Surface Area of Prisms and Cylinders

Review all the entries and read the notes you made in your Tool Kit. Make a list of any questions, terms, or notes you do not understand. Ask your partner or study team members for help. If anything is still unclear, ask your teacher.

# The Jar of Marbles

Chapter 10

# Chapter 10
## *The Jar of Marbles:* PROBABILITY, STATISTICS, AND INTERPRETING DATA

Probability and statistics are useful areas of mathematics. When used to study real data, however, the results can be manipulated in a variety of ways. As a consumer of information through television, the Internet, and printed materials, you should be aware of techniques used to manipulate information and opinions.

In this chapter you will have the opportunity to:

- explore probability through experimentation.

- learn the difference between theoretical and experimental probability.

- classify and calculate independent and dependent probabilities.

- represent possible outcomes in tables, grids, and tree diagrams.

- analyze questions for bias.

- learn to select representative samples.

- classify questions as open or closed option.

- determine whether a correlation exists in a scatter plot.

- determine if causality is reasonable for a given correlation.

Read the problem below, but **do not try to solve it now**. What you learn over the next few days will enable you to solve it.

| JM-0. | How would you ask a survey question and then organize all of the answers you receive into a graph? Would you know whom to ask in order to have a representative sample of the students at your school? Could you ask your question without influencing the person you are interviewing? |  |
|---|---|---|

| | |
|---|---|
| Number Sense | |
| Algebra and Functions | |
| Mathematical Reasoning | |
| Measurement and Geometry | |
| Statistics, Data Analysis, & Probability | |

# Chapter 10
## The Jar of Marbles: PROBABILITY, STATISTICS, AND INTERPRETING DATA

JM-1.   Probability is a topic in mathematics we use almost daily, yet we often do not realize how frequently we use it. Copy and complete these sentences.

   a)   When the weather forecaster says that there is a 20% chance of rain, what is the chance it will not rain?

   b)   If we are <u>certain</u> something will occur, what is the likelihood it will occur?

   c)   If an event is <u>impossible,</u> what is the likelihood of it happening?

   d)   What is the chance of getting heads when you flip a fair coin?

JM-2.   Today you will be recording the results of a coin flipping experiment. Use a coin and the resource page your teacher gives you with a table like the one shown below. Follow these directions for each flip. See the example below.

   a)   You and your partner will flip a coin 25 times. Record the result of each flip.

   b)   In the third column, write the total number of heads up to and including that flip in the numerator of the fraction. The denominator will be the number of the flip.

   c)   After you record each result, convert the fraction to a decimal and a percent.

   Note: An example is shown below. Your actual data will be different.

| Flip Number | Outcome (EXAMPLES!) | Experimental Probability of Heads as a Fraction | Experimental Probability of Heads as a Decimal | Experimental Probability of Heads as a Percent |
|---|---|---|---|---|
| 1 | T | $\frac{0}{1}$ | 0 | 0% |
| 2 | H | $\frac{1}{2}$ | 0.5 | 50% |
| 3 | H | $\frac{2}{3}$ | $0.6\bar{6}$ | $66.\bar{6}\%$ |
| 4 | T | $\frac{2}{4}$ | 0.5 | 50% |

JM-3.    Use your data from coin flipping to answer the questions below, then complete the graph portion of your resource page.

a)    What is the theoretical probability of getting heads?

b)    On the graph paper portion of your resource page, draw a colored horizontal line from 0 to 25 representing the theoretical probability. Include the key on your graph.

c)    In a different color, draw a scatter plot representing the experimental probability of getting heads for your 25 flips. Include this key on your graph as well.

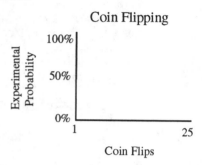

JM-4.    Copy and complete this table using your data from the 25 coin flips. You may need to use proportions to complete it.

| Total Number of Coin Flips | 25 | 50 | 100 | 500 | 1000 |
|---|---|---|---|---|---|
| Number of Heads (based on **experimental** probability) | | | | | |
| Expected Number of Heads (based on **theoretical** probability) | 12.5 | | | | |

JM-5.    Sometimes people say that a fair coin has a 50-50 chance of turning up heads or tails. In other words, in **theory** the two possible **outcomes** are equally likely.

a)    Will an **experiment** of tossing a fair coin always give results that are the same ratio as the **theory**?

b)    If you get heads on one flip, will you always get tails on the second flip?

c)    If you flip a coin 100 times, in theory, how many times do you expect to get heads? Why?

d)    If you flip a coin twice and it comes up heads both times, does this mean the coin is rigged or unfair? Why?

e)    If you flip a coin 100 times and you get 47 heads and 53 tails, does this mean the coin is rigged or unfair? Why?

f)    If you flip a coin 1000 times and get 625 heads and 375 tails, does this mean the coin is rigged or unfair? Why?

JM-6.    In the previous problem you were thinking about two concepts of probability: **theoretical** and **experimental** probabilities.

   a)    While the theoretical probability of getting heads is 50%, what was the experimental probability of getting heads in part (e) of the previous problem?

   b)    On what are theoretical probabilities based?

   c)    On what are experimental probabilities based?

JM-7.

> ## VOCABULARY TERMS FOR PROBABILITY
>
> **SAMPLE SPACE:** All possible outcomes of a situation. For example, there are six possible outcomes when a six-sided die is rolled and two possible outcomes when flipping a coin.
>
> **OUTCOME:** Any possible or actual result or consequence of the action(s) considered, such as rolling a five on a die or getting tails when flipping a coin.
>
> **EVENT:** An outcome or group of outcomes from an experiment, such as rolling an even number on a die.
>
> **PROBABILITY:** A number between zero and one that states the likelihood of an event. It is the ratio of desired outcomes to all possible outcomes (the sample space).
>
> **IMPOSSIBILITY:** When an event has a probability of zero; that is, an event that cannot occur, such as rolling a seven on a six-sided die.
>
> **CERTAINTY:** When an event has a probability of one; such as rolling a number between one and six on a standard die.

Make these notes in your Tool Kit to the right of the double-lined box.

   a)    Describe the sample space when you are dealing from a deck of cards.

   b)    Describe a sample outcome of drawing a card from a full deck.

JM-8.    Find the radius and circumference of the circles with the given area. Use $\pi = 3.14$.

   a)    706.5 ft$^2$                    b)    254.34 m$^2$

JM-9.     Answer these questions about probability.

    a)     What is the highest percent probability you can ever get?

    b)     What is the lowest percent probability you can ever get?

    c)     If the probability of heads is 43.6%, what is the probability of tails?


JM-10.    Find each of the following.

    a)     $|82| - |-20|$                   b)     $|4| - |-40|$

    c)     $|-18| + |63|$                 d)     $|-13.72| + |2.6|$


JM-11.    Write "theoretical" or "experimental" to describe the following statements.

    a)     The chance of getting heads three times in a row when flipping a coin is $\frac{1}{8}$.

    b)     I flipped this coin eight times and got heads six times.

    c)     My mom packed my lunch three of the past five days.

    d)     The chance of finding the winning Zappo Cola can is 1 in 98,000,000.

    e)     Based on mathematical models, the chance of rain today is 60%.

    f)     Based on last year's amount of rain in April, the chance of rain on a day in April this year.

JM-12.    Find the area and perimeter of the following figures. Write the numbers as decimals, rounding to the nearest hundredth.

    a)                                                    b)

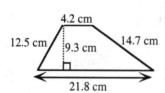

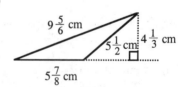

# EXPERIMENTAL AND THEORETICAL PROBABILITIES

**EXPERIMENTAL PROBABILITY** is the probability based on data collected in experiments.

$$\text{Experimental Probability} = \frac{\text{number of successful outcomes in the experiment}}{\text{total number of outcomes in the experiment}}$$

**THEORETICAL PROBABILITY** is a calculated probability based on the possible outcomes when they all have the same chance of occurring.

$$\text{Theoretical Probability} = \frac{\text{number of successful outcomes}}{\text{total number of possible outcomes}}$$

By "successful" we usually mean desired or specified outcome, such as rolling a 3 on a die ($\frac{1}{6}$), pulling a king from a deck of cards ($\frac{4}{52} = \frac{1}{13}$), or flipping a coin and getting tails ($\frac{1}{2}$).

Probabilities are written like this:

The probability of rolling a 3 on a die is P(3).
The probability of pulling a king out of a deck of cards is P(king).
The probability of getting tails is P(tails).

Answer these questions in your Tool Kit to the right of the double-lined box.

a)     For a deck of cards, what is P(diamond)?

b)     For a die, what is P(odd number)?

JM-14.     Now that we have started a new chapter, it is time for you to organize your binder.

a)     Put the work from the last chapter in order and keep it in a separate folder.

b)     When this is completed, write "I have organized my binder."

JM-15.     Follow your teacher's directions for practicing mental math.

JM-16.    Kandi has a bag of marbles. She has 5 black, 3 white, 2 green, and 4 orange marbles. Kandi reaches into the bag without looking and pulls out a marble.

a)    What is the probability that she will pull out a green marble?

b)    If she does get a green marble and does not put it back in the bag, what is the probability she will now pull the other green marble from the bag?

c)    Assume that Kandi does get the second green marble and does not return it to the bag. What is the probability she will now pull another green marble from the bag?

JM-17.    In the previous problem, each event affected the following events because Kandi did <u>not</u> return the marbles to the bag. By taking the green marbles out of the bag, she changed both the numerator and denominator of the later probabilities. However, she did not change the numerator for events like drawing a black marble.

---

### INDEPENDENT AND DEPENDENT EVENTS

Two events are **DEPENDENT** if the outcome of the first event affects the outcome of the second event. For example, if you draw a card from a deck and do not replace it for the next draw, the events are dependent.

Two events are **INDEPENDENT** if the outcome of the first event does not affect the outcome of the second event. For example, if you draw a card from a deck but replace it before you draw again, the two events are independent.

---

Answer these questions in your Tool Kit to the right of the double-lined box.

a)    Is rolling a 3 on a die after you already rolled a 3 an independent or dependent event? Explain.

b)    If you know that Juanito just pulled a green marble from a bag and did not put it back, is pulling another green marble out of the bag an independent or dependent event? Explain.

JM-18. For the following experiments, write "dependent" if the second event depends on the outcome of the first and "independent" if the first event does not affect the outcome of the second event.

a) Flipping a coin and getting tails after you have already flipped it once and gotten tails.

b) Drawing a king from a deck of cards after a card was taken out and not returned to the deck.

c) Drawing an ace from a deck of cards after a card was drawn, replaced, and the deck shuffled again.

d) Getting a peppermint candy from a jar of mixed candies after you just took out and ate a lemon candy.

e) Choose one of the situations described in parts (a) through (d) and explain why you chose either independent or dependent.

JM-19. Think of a standard deck of 52 playing cards[*]. If you pull one card from the deck at random, what is the probability that it is the seven of clubs? (That is, what is P(seven of clubs)?)

$$P(\text{seven of clubs}) = \frac{1 \text{ seven of clubs in the deck}}{52 \text{ possible cards to draw}} = \frac{1}{52} \approx 0.019$$

a) Find P(jack of any suit).

b) Find P(face card).

c) Find P(heart).

d) Are these probabilities theoretical or experimental?

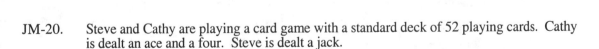

*Note: A standard deck of playing cards has four suits in two colors: diamonds and hearts are red; clubs and spades are black. Each suit has 13 cards: an ace, two through ten, a jack, a queen, and a king. Jacks, queens, and kings are known as "face cards."

JM-20. Steve and Cathy are playing a card game with a standard deck of 52 playing cards. Cathy is dealt an ace and a four. Steve is dealt a jack.

a) How many cards are left in the deck?

b) How many of the remaining cards are aces?

c) If Steve gets an ace, he will win. What is the probability that he will get an ace?

d) Steve gets a two and Cathy gets a five. Now Steve wants a nine. What is the probability that he will get a nine?

JM-21.    Write "theoretical" or "experimental" to
          describe the following statements.

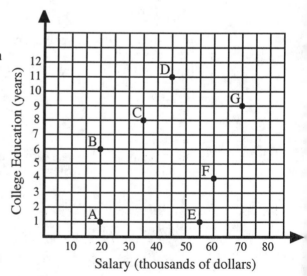

a)    The chance of spinning a four on a spinner
      numbered one through four is $\frac{1}{4}$.

b)    I drew ten cards out of a deck and got
      spades three times.

c)    I made eight out of the last ten free throws.

d)    The chance of winning a new car in the
      raffle is 1 in 32,000.

e)    Based on mathematical models, the chance of a thunderstorm today is 40%.

f)    Based on last year's data, the chance of a hurricane today is 2%.


JM-22.    Find the following probabilities using a standard deck of 52 shuffled playing cards.

a)    Find P(king).

b)    Find P(red eight).

c)    Find P(two or a three).

d)    Are these probabilities theoretical or experimental?  Why?


JM-23.    Answer these questions after studying the graph below.

a)    How many people do you see
      represented on the graph?

b)    Of all the people graphed, which
      person earns the median salary?

c)    Which person has the median
      number of years of college
      education?

d)    What is the mode of the salaries
      shown?

e)    What is the mode of years of
      college education shown in the
      scatter plot?

f)    What is the range of the salaries
      shown?

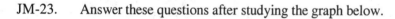

JM-24. Which of the following could <u>not</u> be a probability?

(A)  $-\frac{1}{10}$     (B)  1     (C)  1%     (D)  0.1     (E)  none of these

JM-25. If the experimental probability of getting heads is 75.3%, what is the probability of getting tails?

(A)  75.3% + 100%    (B)  75.3% – 100%    (C)  100% – 75.3%    (D)  $\frac{1}{75.3\%}$

JM-26. Convert each fraction into both a decimal and a percent.

a)  $\frac{2}{5}$      b)  $\frac{2}{6}$      c)  $\frac{5}{8}$      d)  $\frac{8}{12}$

JM-27. Convert each decimal into both a fraction and a percent.

a)  0.1      b)  0.5      c)  $0.\overline{3}$      d)  0.875

JM-28. Complete the following Diamond Problems.

Product

Sum

a)

b)

c)

d)

e)

JM-29. Simplify.

a)  $\frac{11}{12} + \frac{4}{9}$        b)  $4\frac{3}{5} - 1\frac{13}{15}$

c)  $\frac{9}{10} \cdot 2\frac{1}{3}$        d)  $12 \div \frac{7}{8}$

JM-30. Answer these questions about probability.

a)  What is the highest decimal probability you can ever get?

b)  What is the lowest decimal probability you can ever get?

c)  If the decimal probability of getting heads is 0.45, what is P(tails)?

JM-31.    **Marble Probability Experiment**

Your teacher will give you a bag of 20 marbles. Every
team in the class has an identical bag. Do not open or
look inside the bag until you are instructed to do so.
You are going to try to determine how many of each
color marbles there are without looking in the bag.

a)    Each student must create a tally sheet to record the
      number of times each color is pulled out. This can
      be done on scratch paper.

b)    To start the experiment, one student will reach into
      the bag (without looking into it) and take out a
      marble. Each team member records the color of the marble on his/her tally sheet.

c)    The student returns the marble to the bag, gives the bag a gentle shake, then passes
      the bag to the next student. Take turns and repeat the process until you have
      recorded the colors of 40 marbles.

d)    Get a resource page from your teacher. Fill in the team experimental probability
      column on the resource page.

| Event | Your Team's Experimental Probability | Class Experimental Probability | Prediction of Theoretical Probability | Actual Probability |
|---|---|---|---|---|
| purple | $\frac{}{40} = $ % | $\frac{}{40} = $ % | $\frac{}{20} = $ % | $\frac{}{20} = $ % |
| red | $\frac{}{40} = $ % | $\frac{}{40} = $ % | $\frac{}{20} = $ % | $\frac{}{20} = $ % |
| yellow | $\frac{}{40} = $ % | $\frac{}{40} = $ % | $\frac{}{20} = $ % | $\frac{}{20} = $ % |
| orange | $\frac{}{40} = $ % | $\frac{}{40} = $ % | $\frac{}{20} = $ % | $\frac{}{20} = $ % |
| green | $\frac{}{40} = $ % | $\frac{}{40} = $ % | $\frac{}{20} = $ % | $\frac{}{20} = $ % |
| black | $\frac{}{40} = $ % | $\frac{}{40} = $ % | $\frac{}{20} = $ % | $\frac{}{20} = $ % |
| orange or red | $\frac{}{40} = $ % | $\frac{}{40} = $ % | $\frac{}{20} = $ % | $\frac{}{20} = $ % |
| yellow, green, or orange | $\frac{}{40} = $ % | $\frac{}{40} = $ % | $\frac{}{20} = $ % | $\frac{}{20} = $ % |
| not purple | $\frac{}{40} = $ % | $\frac{}{40} = $ % | $\frac{}{20} = $ % | $\frac{}{20} = $ % |
| not red and not purple | $\frac{}{40} = $ % | $\frac{}{40} = $ % | $\frac{}{20} = $ % | $\frac{}{20} = $ % |
| not black | $\frac{}{40} = $ % | $\frac{}{40} = $ % | $\frac{}{20} = $ % | $\frac{}{20} = $ % |

e)    The data your team collected needs to be shared with the rest of the class. Have
      your team representative record your data on the overhead or poster your teacher has
      provided.

f)    Record the class data in the class experimental probability column on your resource
      page.

>>**Problem continues on the next page.**>>

g)     Based on the information you have learned today in your experiment, make an educated guess about the theoretical probabilities, that is, the actual number of marbles of each color in the bag. Record your predictions in the prediction column on your resource page.

h)     After everyone on your team has completed part (g), open the bag and record the actual probabilities in the last column on the resource page.

JM-32.     Now we will calculate probabilities of more complex situations.

a)     Find the sum of the theoretical probabilities for taking out a purple, orange, green, yellow, or red marble.

b)     Explain why the answer to the previous question makes sense.

c)     Why is the probability of (yellow, green, or orange) the same as the probability of (<u>not</u> red and <u>not</u> purple)?

d)     Use your previous answer to help you find another pair of situations with the same probabilities.

JM-33.     Compare your team's experimental probabilities and the class' experimental probabilities with the theoretical probabilities. What conclusion can you make about increasing the number of pieces of data gathered in an experiment?

JM-34.     Busy Lizzie's mom packs her lunch. Lizzie knows that there were five yogurts in the refrigerator: one raspberry, two strawberry, one blueberry, and one vanilla.

a)     Which flavor is she most likely to have in her lunch bag today? Why?

b)     What are her chances of finding a vanilla yogurt in her lunch bag?

JM-35.    Becoming a professional football player is the dream of
          many students.  Here are some numbers to consider.
          There are 265,000 high school seniors who play football
          every year.  16,450 of them make it to a college team.
          215 of those original students make it to a professional
          team.  (Source: NCAA)

a)   Colt is a high school senior on a football team in a
     large city.  There are 1000 seniors playing in his
     league.  Use a proportion to find the number of
     those 1000 students who will make it to a college
     team.

b)   Use a proportion to find the number of those 1000 students who will make it to a
     professional team.

c)   What is the probability that a high school senior football player will make it to a
     professional team?  Express your answer as a percent.

JM-36.    Convert each of the following fractions into a decimal and then into a percent.

a)   $\frac{2}{5}$          b)   $\frac{8}{5}$          c)   $\frac{21}{4}$

d)   $\frac{17}{15}$        e)   $\frac{32}{9}$         f)   $\frac{29}{7}$

JM-37.    If the probability of rain tomorrow is 15%, what is the probability of <u>no</u> rain
          tomorrow?

(A) 0.15 + 1          (B) 0.15 − 1          (C) 1 − 0.15          (D) $\frac{1}{0.15}$

JM-38.    Convert each of the following percents into a decimal and then into a fraction.

a)   25%                                    b)   75%

c)   60%                                    d)   37.5%

JM-39.    A bag of marbles contains only the colors red, green, and blue.

   a)   The probability of getting a red marble is $\frac{1}{3}$. What is the probability of getting a blue or green marble?

   b)   The probability of getting a green marble is $\frac{1}{4}$. What is the probability of getting a blue marble?

   c)   There are 24 marbles in the bag. How many are blue?


JM-40.    Answer these questions using the flow diagram shown below.

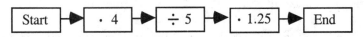

   a)   If you start with 5, with what number do you end?

   b)   If you start with -9, with what number do you end?

   c)   If you start with 10, with what number do you end?

   d)   If you end with 35, with what number did you start?

   e)   Use the word **reciprocal** in a complete sentence to describe what is happening in this flow diagram.


JM-41.    Stephen and Paul saw Doggee Brand Dog Food on sale in a 22-pound bag for $15. They checked the store brand bulk dog food bin and found that the unit price was $0.70 per pound.

   a)   What is the unit cost of Doggee Brand Dog Food?

   b)   Which kind of dog food is the better buy?


JM-42.    Simplify.

   a)   $\frac{5}{8} + \frac{6}{7}$                     b)   $3\frac{14}{15} - \frac{3}{8}$

   c)   $\frac{12}{14} \cdot 2\frac{6}{10}$                     d)   $2\frac{2}{3} \div \frac{5}{7}$


JM-43.    Obtain a poll from your teacher. You will have about five minutes to read and answer the questions. When you are done filling it out, return it to your teacher. When you have finished, write "I took the poll" by this problem number.

JM-44.  Josiah's father likes to create games. His newest game is called Bag of Marbles. There are two purple marbles and one green marble inside a bag. Two players take turns shaking the bag and pulling one marble out of the bag. One player wins a point if the colors match. The other player wins a point if the colors do not match. The first player to earn ten points is the winner.

a)  Decide with your partner who will play for a match and who will play for a no match. Play Bag of Marbles with your partner until one of you wins. Record the results of each draw in your notes by this problem number.

b)  Who won? Match or no match?

c)  Do you think match or no match has an advantage or are they equally likely?

JM-45.  Josiah and his father are going to play Bag of Marbles tonight. The loser has to wash all the dishes the next day. Knowing the stakes, Josiah wants to figure out whether match or no match has an advantage.

a)  Josiah decided to look at this problem by making a table. He uses the letter G for the green marble and the letter P for the purple marbles. Why did Josiah label one side of his table "First Shake" and the other side "Second Shake"? Explain.

|  | Second Shake | | |
|---|---|---|---|
| First Shake | G | P | P |
| G |  |  |  |
| P |  |  |  |
| P |  |  |  |

b)  Why did Josiah put two Ps on each side? Explain.

c)  Fill in each box in Josiah's table using G and P.

d)  Knowing each square is equally likely, what is the probability of winning if you play for a match? That is, what is P(match)?

e)  What is the probability of winning if you play for no match? That is, what is P(no match)?

f)  Should Josiah choose match or no match? Explain.

JM-46.  Josiah's best friend Antonio came to Josiah's house and saw his table for "Bag of Marbles." Antonio said, "Josiah, you've done it wrong. Use generic rectangles. There are only two colors, so it doesn't matter whether you play for a match or not."

|  | Second Shake | |
|---|---|---|
| First Shake | G | P |
| G |  |  |
| P |  |  |

a)  Fill in Antonio's table.

b)  How are the two tables different?

c)  According to Antonio's table, what is the probability of winning if you play for a match?

d)  According to Antonio's table, what is the probability of winning if you play for no match?

e)  Which table is correct if you use two purple marbles and only one green marble? Why?

JM-47. Josiah's father walked in and looked at Antonio's table. He said, "We can use your table accurately if we fill in the table with fractions, similar to a generic rectangle." Josiah's dad changed the table as shown at right.

Second Shake

|  | $G \frac{1}{3}$ | $P \frac{2}{3}$ |
|---|---|---|
| $G \frac{1}{3}$ | $GG \frac{1}{9}$ | $GP \frac{2}{9}$ |
| $P \frac{2}{3}$ | $PG \frac{2}{9}$ | $PP \frac{4}{9}$ |

(First Shake labels the left column.)

a) Why did Josiah's dad write $\frac{1}{3}$ next to the G?

b) Why did Josiah's dad write $\frac{2}{3}$ next to the two Ps?

c) Write a complete sentence to explain each of the fractions inside the boxes in this new table.

d) According to this table, should Josiah play for match or no match? Why?

e) Does Josiah's table in problem JM-45 agree with his dad's table in this problem? Explain.

JM-48. Write "theoretical" or "experimental" to describe the following statements.

a) The chance of rolling a sum of three with two dice is $\frac{1}{18}$.

b) I drew five cards out of a deck and got clubs three times.

c) I bought six raffle tickets and did not win anything.

d) Based on mathematical models, the chance of a thunderstorm today is 40%.

JM-49. Why is the statement "It always rains on my birthday" a statement of experimental probability rather than of theoretical probability?

JM-50. For the following experiments, write "dependent" if the second event depends on the outcome of the first event and "independent" if the second event does not depend on the outcome of the first event.

a) P(spinning spin a two on a spinner after having just spun a two)

b) P(drawing a red six from a deck of cards after a card was just drawn and not returned to the deck)

c) P(drawing a face card from a deck of cards after a jack was just drawn and replaced and the deck shuffled again)

d) P(getting a lemon-lime soda if the person before you reaches into a cooler full of lemon-lime sodas, removes one, and drinks it)

JM-51.  If the probability of getting a red marble from a bag is $\frac{3}{8}$, what is the probability of not getting a red marble?

(A) $1 - \frac{3}{8}$      (B) $\frac{3}{8} - 1$      (C) $1 + \frac{3}{8}$      (D) $1\frac{3}{8}$

JM-52. Find the area of the shapes with the following dimensions:

a) a triangle with a height of 4.7 inches and a base of 6.8 inches

b) a rectangle with a length of 12.4 meters and a width of 8.7 meters

c) a triangle with a height of 7.4 feet and a base of 5.9 feet

d) a square with a side length of 7.3 centimeters

JM-53. Solve the following problem by writing and solving an equation or by using a Guess and Check table. Remember to write your answer in a complete sentence.

A triangle with a perimeter of 16.3 centimeters has one side that is two times the length of another side. The third side is 1.7 centimeters longer than the shortest side. Find the lengths of the sides of the triangle.

JM-54. **Algebra Puzzles** Solve the following problems.

a) $-4(5x + 11) = 128$

b) $x + 16 + 2x - 21 = 40$

c) $41 + 3x - 17 + 5x = 24$

d) $4(3x - 7) + 25 = -39$

JM-55. Simplify.

a) $2\frac{1}{2} - \frac{3}{5}$

b) $6 \div 3\frac{2}{3}$

c) $2\frac{1}{4} \cdot 8\frac{1}{2}$

JM-56.   Here is a graphical look at proportions and percents.  Copy and complete the table.

| Picture | Problem in Words / Proportion | Answer |
|---|---|---|
| 20 ⌐ 100% <br> 15 ⌐ n% <br> 0 ⌐ 0% | What percent of 20 is 15? <br><br> $\dfrac{15 \text{ part}}{20 \text{ whole}} = \dfrac{n \text{ part}}{100\% \text{ whole}}$ | |
| 30 ⌐ 100% <br> 24 ⌐ n% <br> 0 ⌐ 0% | $\dfrac{\phantom{xxx}}{\phantom{xxx}} = \dfrac{\phantom{xxx}}{\phantom{xxx}}$ | |

JM-57.   Find the fraction greater than $\frac{1}{4}$ and less than $\frac{3}{10}$ that has the smallest possible denominator.

JM-58.   Copy and complete this table using the fractions your teacher will provide.

| Question | Event To Examine | Poll A Fraction | Poll A Percent | Poll B Fraction | Poll B Percent |
|---|---|---|---|---|---|
| 1. Name anything teenagers worry about. | grades/graduation | | | | |
| 2. Do you support the President's Education Plan? | yes | | | | |
| 3. How could education in America be improved? | more computer spending | | | | |
| 4. Do you think violence in movies affects children? | yes | | | | |
| 5. Should teachers make more money? | yes | | | | |
| 6. Do you like exercise? | yes | | | | |

JM-59.   Were the results from Poll A and Poll B similar?  List any reasons you think might account for the differences.

JM-60. Let's examine each of the questions to find possible reasons for the different results we obtained. Here are the six questions as they were presented to each team.

| Poll A | Poll B |
|---|---|
| 1. To what level do teenagers worry about poor grades? (low / medium / high) <br><br> What do teenagers worry about these days? | 1. Name one thing teenagers worry about these days. |
| 2. Do you support the President's education plan? | 2. Do you support the President's education plan since it will ensure that students will be more successful in school? |
| 3. How could education in America be improved? ___ <br><br> a) develop higher standards for students <br> b) raise teacher salaries <br> c) make more computers accessible to students <br> d) other (specify) | 3. How could education in America be improved? <br><br> |
| 4. Do you think violence in today's movies affects children? | 4. Do you think the frequent occurrence of brutal violence in today's movies affects young, impressionable children? |
| 5. Should teachers make more money? | 5. Don't you agree that teachers should make more money? |
| 6. Moderate exercise is necessary to stay healthy. Do you exercise? | 6. Do you exercise? |

a) **Question Order:** Question 1 uses this technique to bias or influence the results. This means that two questions were asked in order so that the first one suggests the answer to the second. Which poll in Question 1, A or B, used the "question order" technique and why is it going to influence responses?

b) **Preface:** Instead of asking a question, these questions usually start with statements that can bias the result of the following question. Which question number (2 through 6) and poll letter (A or B) used this technique?

c) **Two Questions in One:** This technique involves asking two questions at once. The people being asked may agree with one part and disagree with another part, but they are not allowed to give a separate answer for each part. Which question number (2 through 6) and poll letter (A or B) used this technique?

>>Problem continues on the next page.>>

d) **Closed Option:** If a person only has a few choices, this increases the chance a certain choice will be picked. Which question number (2 through 6) and poll letter (A or B) used this technique?

e) **Favorable Or Unfavorable Wording:** By using adjectives, pleasing or unpleasant words, the surveyor can influence the results. Which question number (2 through 6) and poll letter (A or B) used this technique?

f) **Desire To Please:** Most people want to be agreeable and please the surveyor. Any questions starting with, "Don't you agree" or "Don't you think" are naturally biased. Which question number (2 through 6) and poll letter (A or B) used this technique?

JM-61.  Armando and Vlad were flipping three coins: a nickel, a dime, and a quarter.

a) Make an organized list of the possible outcomes. If the nickel comes up heads, the dime comes up heads, and the quarter comes up tails, we write this outcome as HHT.

b) They decided that Armando would win when exactly two heads come up and Vlad would win if exactly one head comes up. Who has a better chance of winning? Explain.

JM-62.  Sharee, who was working on the previous problem, suggested, "It's hard to keep track of the possibilities in a list. Let's make a grid."

a) Explain why it would be difficult to use a grid with this problem.

b) Dexter did not think that a grid would work. He started drawing a different kind of diagram, called a **tree diagram**. He explained that the first split showed the two choices for the nickel; it could be heads (H) or tails (T). If the nickel was heads, then the second split would show the two choices for the dime. The same is true if the nickel was tails. The third split is for quarters. What outcome does HHT represent?

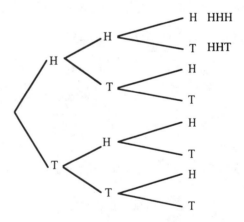

c) Copy his diagram and complete the list of outcomes at the side.

d) Where does Dexter's diagram show the outcome that the nickel was tails while the dime and quarter were both heads?

e) On your diagram, circle the outcome(s) with exactly two heads. What is the probability of flipping exactly two heads?

JM-63.    Steve is playing another card game with Cathy. They shuffle 52 cards. Cathy is dealt a
          three and a five, while Steve is dealt a five and a ten. None of the cards are returned to the
          deck.

          a)    What is the probability that Steve will get a six on his next card?

          b)    Continuing their game, Steve gets a three and Cathy gets a five. Now Steve
                wants another three. What is the probability that he will get a three?


JM-64.    Kimberly has a pair of dice. To win the game she is playing she needs to roll a sum of
          five on her next turn. She made the following chart of the possible sums of two dice.

First Die Roll

| + | 1 | 2 | 3 | 4 | 5 | 6 |
|---|---|---|---|---|---|---|
| 1 | 2 | 3 | 4 | 5 | 6 | 7 |
| 2 | 3 | 4 | 5 | 6 | 7 | 8 |
| 3 | 4 | 5 | 6 | 7 | 8 | 9 |
| 4 | 5 | 6 | 7 | 8 | 9 | 10 |
| 5 | 6 | 7 | 8 | 9 | 10 | 11 |
| 6 | 7 | 8 | 9 | 10 | 11 | 12 |

Second Die Roll

The two dice are
rolled, and the
sum is shown
here.
◀

          a)    How many squares representing sums are shown in the table?

          b)    How many of the squares show a sum of five?

          c)    What is the probability that she will roll a sum of five?

          d)    What is the probability that she will roll a sum greater than five?

          e)    If she rolls a sum of five on her first roll, what is the probability that she will roll a
                sum of five on her second roll?


JM-65.    A bag of marbles contains only the colors yellow, green, and blue.

          a)    The probability of getting a yellow marble is $\frac{2}{3}$. What is the probability of getting a
                blue or green marble?

          b)    The probability of getting a green marble is $\frac{1}{4}$. What is the probability of getting a
                blue marble?

          c)    There are 24 marbles in the bag. How many are blue?

JM-66.    In your own words answer the following questions.

   a)    Is there an x such that $|x| = -1$? Explain your reasoning.

   b)    If $|x| = 3$ what are the possible values for x?

   c)    What is your best definition of absolute value?


JM-67.    Which of the values below <u>cannot</u> be a probability?

   (A)   0        (B)   $\frac{3}{8}$        (C)   45%        (D)   1.2        (E)   none of these


JM-68.    While computing the statistics of his baseball team, Jake found that Geraldo was getting a hit 5 out of 7 times at bat. Approximately how many hits would Geraldo get if he were at bat 100 times?


JM-69.    If baseball were played on Mars, the balls would fly much farther than they do on Earth. Thus, the number of home runs would be much greater on Mars. If Mike hit 76 homers on Earth, he could expect to hit 50% more on Mars. How many home runs would he hit on Mars?


JM-70.    Solve for  x.

   a)   $\frac{1}{2} = \frac{x}{10}$        b)   $\frac{x}{55} = \frac{5}{10}$        c)   $\frac{45}{63} = \frac{10}{x}$

   d)   $\frac{36}{x} = \frac{5.4}{2.4}$        e)   $\frac{42}{14.7} = \frac{x}{7}$        f)   $\frac{x}{15} = \frac{2.7}{3}$


JM-71.    Answer these questions using the flow diagram shown below.

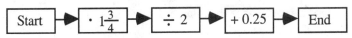

   a)    If you start with 8, with what number do you end?

   b)    If you start with -12, with what number do you end?

   c)    If you start with $\frac{1}{2}$, with what number do you end?

   d)    If you <u>end</u> with 1.25, with what fraction did you start?

   e)    If you <u>end</u> with $\frac{13}{24}$, with what fraction did you start?

JM-72.    Here is a graphical look at proportions and percents.  Copy and complete the table.

| Picture | Problem in Words / Proportion | Answer |
|---|---|---|
| 40 ⎯ 100%<br>n ⎯ 55%<br>0 ⎯ 0% | What is 55% of 40?<br><br>——— = ——— | |
| 80 ⎯ 100%<br>50 ⎯ n%<br>0 ⎯ 0% | | |

JM-73.    Solve for the variable.

a)    $3b - 2b + 17 + \frac{1}{4}b = 18$          b)    $5(6 - x) + 2.5(x + 2) = 25$

c)    $0.7(m - 10) = -6$                         d)    $1.8(2n - 5) = -12.6$

JM-74.    Find the area and circumference of a circle with a radius of 6.3 centimeters.

JM-75.    Here are some questions.  Identify which of the six techniques is being used to try to influence the people being surveyed.  If no bias technique is being used, write, "Fair question."

a)    Zappo Cola has twice the vitamin E of other brands.  In your opinion, what is the healthiest cola drink?

b)    Do you think that cruel people who hurt defenseless animals should be imprisoned?

c)    Don't you agree that Hal Poppington is the best man to be Mayor?

d)    Which soda is your favorite?

e)    Which shirt color would you prefer?  1) blue  2) beige  3) brown  4) tan

JM-76. You and your partner work for the U.S. Department of Education. You have been asked to survey people about the President's new proposal to have students attend school for 200 days instead of 180 days. A fair question would be, "Do you think students should attend school for 180 days, as they do now, or for 200 days?" Rewrite the fair question to bias (or influence) the results toward the 200 day answer. Each team will work on one of the following.

    a)    Order Of Question          b)    Two Questions In One

    c)    Closed Option              d)    Unfavorable Or Favorable Wording

    e)    Desire To Please           f)    Preface

JM-77. Today we will begin our survey project. Your teacher will give you a choice of questions and further instructions. You will attempt to learn what all the students in your school think about the question by surveying a **representative sample**. You will calculate the percent of students who give you different answers and keep track of characteristics of your **sample population**.

After your teacher offers you a choice of survey questions, copy down the question you chose by this problem number.

JM-78. Copy the timeline for the project in your notes or assignment calendar. Write the dates your teacher gives you for each of the following.

    a)    Survey questions chosen.

    b)    Modifications approved, tally form created, student survey started.

    c)    Student survey finished, all percents calculated, graph drawn.

JM-79. Survey questions can be either **open** or **closed**. Open questions allow free response. The responses from open questions are frequently difficult to organize. Closed questions allow only a limited number of responses, which the researcher knows before doing the survey. Classify the following questions as either "open" or "closed."

    a)    What date is your birthday?

    b)    Who is your favorite actor?

    c)    What adjective would you use to describe your best friend?

    d)    What is your favorite day of the week?

JM-80.    Read your survey question again.

    a)    Is your survey question open or closed?

    b)    Will you have difficulty organizing the responses from your question?

    c)    Would it be easier to create a closed list of possible answers to make the responses easier to organize?

    d)    Will it be possible to categorize the responses from your question?

    e)    If you need to rewrite or change your question, do so by tomorrow and make sure your teacher approves the changes you make.

JM-81.    Complete a tree diagram to show the outcomes for the first Bag of Marbles game Josiah and his dad played in problem JM-45. The tree is started at right.

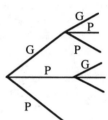

    a)    Does this tree give us the same set of outcomes as the grid?

    b)    The tree can also be made using just one P for purple marbles, provided you use the probabilities. Draw the tree at right including the probabilities.

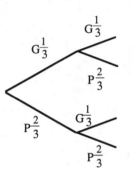

    c)    What do you need to do to calculate the probability of drawing two purple marbles?

    d)    What do you need to do to calculate the probability of drawing two green marbles.

    e)    Show how to calculate the probability of a match. That is, P(match).

    f)    Show how to calculate P(no match).

JM-82.    Convert each of the following fractions into a decimal and then into a percent.

    a)    $\frac{125}{75}$                b)    $\frac{8}{9}$                c)    $\frac{5}{11}$

    d)    $\frac{42}{43}$                e)    $\frac{37}{38}$                f)    $\frac{21}{17}$

JM-83. Josiah played the marble game and chose to play for a match. His father ended up washing the dishes the next day. Josiah's father decided to build a new bag of marbles. He put in one green and three purple marbles.

a) Copy and complete a table like the one below to analyze the advantages of playing each strategy with this new bag.

|   | G | P | P | P |
|---|---|---|---|---|
| G | GG match | | | |
| P | GP no match | | | |
| P | | | | |
| P | | | | |

b) Use your table from part (a) to determine the probability of getting match and getting no match.

c) Which strategy from part (b) has a greater probability of winning?

d) Draw a generic rectangle fraction table to analyze the advantages of playing match with the new bag.

e) Should Josiah play match or no match? What are the probabilities?

JM-84. During the 162-game baseball season, the outfielder Felipe saved an average of $32 per game. He kept the money in a sock in his locker.

a) At the end of the season he took his money to the bank. How much had he saved by the end of the season?

b) He plans to leave all the money in his savings account until the end of next season. At a simple interest rate of 4.68% per year, how much will he have at the end of next season?

JM-85. Amanda and her family went to a restaurant for dinner. The meal cost $27.96. They want to leave a tip between 15% and 20%. How much should they leave? Explain how you found your answer.

JM-86.    The Fibonnacis bought new shoes for the Little
          League team.  They found the shoes at a 25% off
          sale.  The shoes originally cost $28.95.

a)    How much did they save on each pair?

b)    How much did they pay for each pair?

c)    What was the total cost for ten pairs of shoes?

d)    Sales tax is 7.5%.  How much was the tax on
      the ten pairs of shoes?

e)    What was the total cost for the ten pairs of shoes?


JM-87.    Here is a graphical representation of proportions and percents.  Copy and complete the table.

| Picture | Problem in Words / Proportion | Answer |
|---------|-------------------------------|--------|
| 400 — 100%<br>n — 15%<br>0 — 0% | | |
| n — 100%<br>85 — 24%<br>0 — 0% | | |

JM-88.   You should have revised your survey question and obtained your teacher's approval for your changes. To help you survey students in an organized manner, you need to set up a table to keep track of the participants.

a)   Take out a sheet of binder paper. Write your question and heading at the top of the page.

b)   Make a list of four characteristics of your school's population you will monitor in your sample to ensure that your sample is representative (i.e., gender, age, grade, location, whether or not you know the person, etc.).

c)   Set up a table that you will use to record each student's characteristics and responses. You will turn this paper in on the due date. Look at the sample form below.

| My Question: What is your favorite color? | | | | | |
|---|---|---|---|---|---|
| # | Name | Gender | Know Them? | Rides Bike | Area Asked | Response |
| 1 | Kim | F | yes | no | classroom | blue |
| 2 | Scott | M | no | yes | bus | red |
| | | | | | | |

d)   Your teacher will tell you the number of students you need to survey. Number your table accordingly.

JM-89.   Your survey is supposed to represent the entire **population** of students in your school. Will you be able to ask your question of <u>every</u> student in your school? Why or why not?

JM-90.   If you want to know what a dish of food tastes like, you can get a good idea by trying a little taste or a **sample** of the food. You do not need to eat the whole dish of food. When statisticians cannot survey everyone in a **population**, they use a **sample** of the population. However, getting a **representative sample** is not always easy.

a)   If you wanted to generalize the opinions of all students at your school, would it make sense to go to a bank and survey the people there? Why or why not?

b)   If you wanted to generalize the opinions of all students at your school, would it make sense to ask all your friends at school? Why or why not?

c)   If you wanted to generalize the opinions of all students at your school, would it make sense to ask every third person in the bus line?

JM-91.

Highlight the key words of each of the three definitions in your Tool Kit.

JM-92.    There are a variety of ways to sample the population you are studying. Each method has advantages and drawbacks.

a)    If you ask the opinion of the people around you, then you have conducted a **convenience sample**. What is a feature of a convenience sample?

b)    What is a drawback to a convenience sample?

c)    If you mail a questionnaire and accept all the returned responses, then you have taken a **written survey**. What is a feature of a written survey?

d)    What is a drawback to a written survey?

e)    If you systematically choose random people from your population, then you have a **random sample**. What is a feature of a random sample?

f)    What is a drawback to a random sample?

JM-93.    From what population are each of these samples taken? Write down the actual population for each of these sampling techniques.

| Method of Sampling | Description of Actual Population |
|---|---|
| Call every hundredth name in the phone book. | People with phones who have their number listed. |
| Call people at home at 10 a.m. | |
| Ask every tenth person who leaves the mall. | |
| Ask people leaving the bank. | |
| Mail questionnaires to people. | |
| Ask everyone on the school bus. | |

JM-94.    In 1988 the Steering Committee of the
          Physicians Health Study Research Group
          released the results of a five-year experiment
          on over 22,000 male physicians aged 40 to 84.
          The research on this sample suggested that the
          participants who took an aspirin every other
          day had a lower rate of heart attacks.

a)    Can you legitimately conclude from this
      sample that aspirin reduces heart attacks
      for all men and women?  If you cannot
      conclude this, why not?

b)    Can you legitimately conclude from this sample that aspirin reduces heart attacks for
      all men?  If you cannot conclude this, why not?

c)    Can you legitimately conclude from this sample that aspirin reduces heart attacks for
      all men aged 40 to 84?  If you cannot conclude this, why not?

d)    Can you legitimately conclude from this sample that aspirin reduces heart attacks for
      male physicians aged 40 to 84?  If you cannot conclude this, why not?

e)    Can you legitimately conclude from this sample that aspirin is good for male
      physicians aged 40 to 84?  If you cannot conclude this, why not?


JM-95.    At right is a graph of seven coordinate points.

a)    Look at the points in the graph and organize the
      ordered pairs in a table.

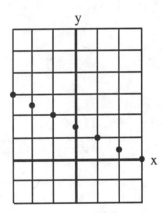

      Example:

| x | -3 | -2 | -1 | 0 | 1 | 2 | 3 |
|---|----|----|----|----|----|----|----|
| y |    | 2.5 |   |   |   |   |   |

b)    What algebraic rule would give these points?

c)    Name at least two other points which
      would fit this rule.

JM-96.    For your survey, you will need to sample students carefully to get a representative sample of the population.

a)    Why would your survey not be representative if you only call your friends?

b)    Why would your survey not be representative if you survey only students in your math class?

c)    Why would your survey not be representative if you survey only students in the bicycle area?

d)    Why would your survey not be representative if you survey only boys?

e)    Make a list of three things you will do when asking people your survey question to ensure you are asking a representative sample of the student population.


JM-97.    Find the value of each expression.

a)    $\frac{1}{3} - (-\frac{3}{4})$

b)    $\frac{2}{3}(-\frac{3}{5})$

c)    $\frac{2}{3} - \frac{4}{5}$

d)    $-\frac{4}{7} \cdot \frac{5}{8}$

e)    $1\frac{2}{3} \cdot 4$

f)    $-1\frac{1}{4}(-2\frac{4}{7})$


JM-98.    Find the radius and circumference of the circles with the given area. Use a calculator and round to the nearest hundredth.

a)    100.81 yd$^2$

b)    550 km$^2$


JM-99.    Angela and Kenya were trying to figure out how many cupboard handles to buy in order to remodel the kitchen. The new cupboards would only need 50% as many handles as the old ones. Show the proportions and answer the questions below.

a)    If 38 handles were needed for all of the new cupboards, how many handles were on the original cupboards?

b)    The cost of each new handle was the same as the cost of each original handle. If the original handles cost a total of $338, what will be the cost of the new handles?

c)    When they got to the hardware store, they found the handles were 25% off. How much will it cost them to purchase the new cupboard handles?

**JM-100.** Here is a graphical representation of proportions and percents. Copy and complete the table. Round to the nearest hundredth.

| Picture | Problem in Words / Proportion | Answer |
|---|---|---|
| n 132 — 100% 92%  0 — 0% | 132 is 92% of what number?  $\underline{\hspace{2cm}} = \underline{\hspace{2cm}}$ | |
| n 24 — 100% 85%  0 — 0% | | |

**JM-101.** Follow your teacher's directions for practicing mental math.

**JM-102.** A good surveyor tries to keep the people being surveyed from being biased by prior experience. For this problem, assume you are conducting a taste test to compare Zappo Cola and Fizzy Cola.

    a)    How would you make sure that people's preconceived notions of their favorite soda would not be an influencing factor?

    b)    If four people all taste the two sodas simultaneously, how can you make sure they do not influence each other's opinions by talking about their impressions?

    c)    Could the temperature of the colas make a difference? How would you reduce any influence that temperature could have?

**JM-103.** You have studied a number of ways to organize data visually.

    a)    Make a list of all the different types of graphs you know how to make.

    b)    Which of the graphs you listed in part (a) will you use to present your data from the survey question you were assigned?

    c)    In how many days is your survey due?

JM-104. At the school fair students played a game called Flip and Spin where first you flip a coin and then you spin a spinner. If you flip heads and then spin red, you win a small stuffed animal. If you flip tails and then spin yellow, you win another turn to play.

a) Make a tree diagram to represent the problem.

b) Show how to use your tree diagram to calculate the probability that you will win a stuffed animal on the first play.

c) Use a grid to represent the problem.

d) Show how to use your grid to calculate the probability that you will win a stuffed animal on the first play.

e) Which model do you prefer to use, the tree diagram or the grid? Why?

JM-105. Your project is due very soon! Here is a list of things you need to finish before the due date.

a) If you have not finished sampling students, do so now. Be prepared to turn in your tally sheet.

b) Create a graph of student responses. You may need to categorize data. Your graph should be visually neat and clear and easy to read from a distance.

c) On a separate piece of paper show your work for these questions.

  i) Calculate the percent of the sample giving each of the responses. (Example: 25% of the sample chose green as their favorite color.)

  ii) How did you ensure a random, representative sample of the population?

  iii) What were the characteristics you monitored when establishing a representative sample?

  iv) Calculate the percent of your sample with each of the characteristics you listed in part (iii). Example: 54% of the sample were students I knew.

JM-106. In the previous chapter, you studied the area of a circle, $A = \pi r^2$. For this problem we use the variables x and y instead of A and r.

a) Create a table to organize a set of points which follow the rule $y = \pi x^2$. Use $\pi = \frac{22}{7}$. Graph the ordered pairs on a coordinate grid.

b) What do the x-values represent?

c) What do the y-values represent?

JM-107. Find the value of each expression.

a) 18 + (-33)

b) 14 · (-5)

c) (-16) ÷ 8

d) -28 + 45

e) (-23) · (-6)

f) -26 + (-37)

JM-108. Melissa is going to re-sod her yard. Her backyard has a rectangular lawn area that is $24\frac{1}{2}$ feet by 18 feet. Her front yard has two rectangular areas. One is $18\frac{1}{2}$ feet by $14\frac{1}{2}$ feet, and the other is $12\frac{1}{2}$ feet by $14\frac{1}{2}$ feet. How many square feet of sod does Melissa need?

JM-109. The town Little League needed more baseball bats. Bats normally cost $25 each. Because it is late in the season, the sporting goods company is having a half-price sale. It is such a good deal that the league decides to stock up for the next season and buy fifty bats. What is their total bill? (Do not forget to add the sales tax of 7.5%.)

JM-110. Complete the following Diamond Problems.

Product
Sum

a)

b)

c)

d)

e)

JM-111. Here is a graphical representation of proportions and percents. Copy and complete the tab[le]

| Picture | Problem in Words / Proportion | Answer |
|---|---|---|
| 400 ⊢ 100% <br> 215 ▓ n% <br> 0 ▓ 0% | ——— = ——— | |
| n ⊢ 100% <br> 120 ▓ 75% <br> 0 ▓ 0% | ——— = ——— | |

JM-112. Mentally calculate 60% of $37. Write your result and explain how you got it.

JM-113. Calculate the following sums and differences.

a)  $\dfrac{5}{7} + \dfrac{4}{5}$

b)  $\dfrac{11}{15} + \dfrac{4}{11}$

c)  $\dfrac{11}{15} - \dfrac{4}{11}$

JM-114. Are the following relationships possible or not possible? Explain your answer in a complete sentence.

a)  An increase in the number of pages in a book causes an increase in the cost of the book.

b)  An increase in shoe size causes an increase in spelling ability.

c)  An increase in the number of years of education causes an increase in salary.

d)  An increase in facial tissue sales causes an increase in hot chocolate sales.

e)  An increase in walking time causes an increase in weight loss.

f)  An increase in a husband's age causes an increase in the wife's age.

JM-115.  Examine the scatter plot below which shows the number of pages in a book compared to the price of the book.

a)  How many books are represented in this scatter plot?

b)  Is this correlation **positive**? (As one variable increases in value, does the other variable increase as well?)

c)  What does this graph tell you about the relationship between the number of pages in the book and its price?

d)  Does an increase in the number of pages cause an increase in the price?

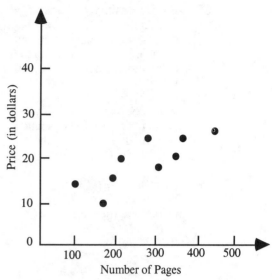

JM-116.  Graph the following data as a scatter plot on the resource page.

a)  Is the correlation positive? (As one value increases, does the other value also increase?)

b)  In your opinion, does more time studying cause a rise in test scores?

| Hours Spent Studying | Test Scores (Percent) |
|---|---|
| 10 | 90 |
| $5\frac{1}{2}$ | 70 |
| 12 | 97 |
| 7 | 85 |
| 6 | 80 |
| $2\frac{2}{3}$ | 55 |
| 15 | 100 |
| 1 | 20 |
| 10 | 85 |
| 4 | 70 |
| 8 | 85 |

JM-117.    Look at the scatter plot below showing the husband's age compared to the wife's age.

a)    Is this a positive or negative correlation?  A **negative correlation** means that as one variable increases in value, the other variable decreases in value.

b)    What does the graph tell you about the age of the husband compared to the age of the wife?

c)    Does an increase in the husband's age cause an increase in the wife's age?

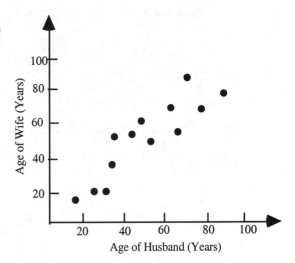

JM-118.    In the preceding problem, the events are not caused by each other; each one is caused by another factor.  Look at the double-line graph below to answer the following questions.

a)    Do the sales of tissues and hot chocolate appear to be correlated or somehow connected?

b)    Does the sale of tissue <u>cause</u> the increase in the sale of hot chocolate? Explain.

c)    Why does the data seem to be related as it appears in the line graph?

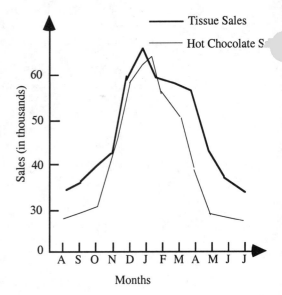

JM-119.   Graph the following data as a scatter plot on the resource page.

a)   Is the correlation positive or negative?

b)   Does there appear to be a connection between height and spelling ability?

c)   Does more height cause better spelling ability?

d)   What other factors could create the correlation you see?

| Height | Spelling Test (Percent) |
|--------|-------------------------|
| 24 | 3 |
| 56 | 86 |
| 72 | 98 |
| 49 | 50 |
| 18 | 0 |
| 36 | 12 |
| 70 | 90 |
| 66 | 81 |
| 61 | 75 |
| 34 | 25 |
| 59 | 80 |
| 57 | 77 |
| 64 | 88 |

JM-120.   Find the diameter of the circles with the given circumference. Use $\pi = \frac{22}{7}$.

a)   1331 m

b)   770 in.

c)   99.88 cm

d)   5280 km

JM-121.   Sometimes we notice that two things are connected, and we assume that the connection means that one thing causes the other. For example, if you study enough people, you may notice that the more gray hairs a person has the fewer hours the person spends at work. Does this mean gray hair causes people to work less? Explain the real connection described here.

JM-122.   Look back at problem JM-116 to answer the following questions.

a)   How many people are represented in the graph?

b)   Find the mean number of hours spent studying.

c)   Find the median of the test scores.

d)   Why is the mean not the best measure for the test scores?

JM-123.  Here is a graphical representation of proportions and percents.  Copy and complete the tab!

| Picture | Problem in Words / Proportion | Answer |
|---|---|---|
| 400 — 100%<br>384 — n%<br><br>0 — 0% | | |
| n — 100%<br><br>90 — 25%<br>0 — 0% | | |

JM-124.  Find the area and circumference of a circle with a diameter of 23.8 inches.

JM-125.  Simplify the following expressions.

a)  $(6 - 8)(9 - 10) - (4 + 2)(6 + 3)$

b)  $\dfrac{-84}{32 - 12(-5)}$

c)  $-4 \cdot 7 + 2(-3\frac{1}{8})$

d)  $56 - (-4) + (-6)(4\frac{2}{3})$

JM-126.  Simplify.

a)  $2\frac{7}{8} + \frac{3}{5}$

b)  $\frac{9}{12} - \frac{5}{8}$

c)  $4\frac{4}{5} \cdot \frac{6}{7}$

d)  $\frac{3}{8} \div 6\frac{3}{4}$

JM-127.  In a jar you have ten cubes numbered 0, 1, 2, ... , 9. Take out a cube, write the number down, put it back in the jar, shake the jar, and take out a cube again. What is the probability that the sum of the two cubes is 10 or greater?

JM-128. Today you will present your survey projects in class. Be sure you have the following items ready to turn in as directed by your teacher:

a) tally sheet

b) graph of responses

c) calculations and explanations from problem JM-105 part (c).

JM-129. **Chapter Summary** Answering the following questions will help you to summarize this chapter. Write a paragraph about:

a) how theoretical and experimental probabilities are calculated.

b) when experimental probabilities are likely to be close to the theoretical probability.

Use three ways to organize and solve the following probability problem: a list, a grid or generic rectangle, and a tree diagram.

c) Josiah's dad thinks he has finally figured out a way to win the marble match game. He decided to use two bags, one with three purple marbles and one green marble. The other bag has one purple marble and two green marbles. Each player draws two marbles, one from each bag. Analyze this game. Who has a better chance, Josiah playing for match or his dad playing for no match?

d) Explain which method you prefer to use when analyzing problems like (c).

JM-130. Here is a graphical representation of proportions and percents. Copy and complete the tabl'

| Picture | Problem in Words / Proportion | Answer |
|---------|-------------------------------|--------|
| 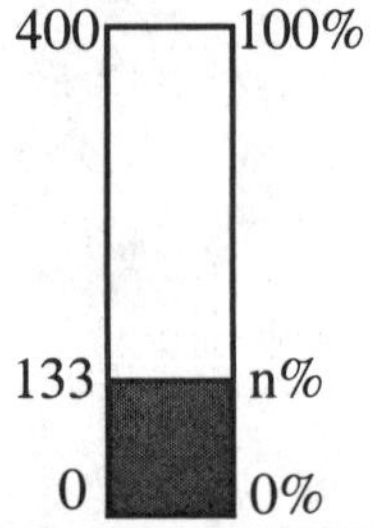 400 ⌐ ¬100%<br><br><br>133 ▓ n%<br>0 ▓ 0% | $\underline{\hphantom{xxx}} = \underline{\hphantom{xxx}}$ | |
| 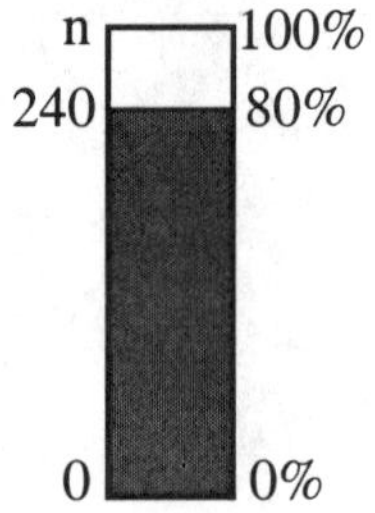 n ⌐ ¬100%<br>240 ▓ 80%<br><br><br><br>0 ▓ 0% | | |

JM-131.  Compute the following percentages.

a)   25% of 80

b)   $12\frac{1}{2}\%$ of  120

c)   $33\frac{1}{3}\%$ of 75

d)   60% of 70

e)   15% of 60

f)   9% of 1015

JM-132.  Evaluate the following expressions.

a)   $\frac{2}{5} \cdot \frac{3}{7}$

b)   $\frac{3}{4} + \frac{5}{6} + \frac{2}{3}$

c)   $\frac{3}{8} \div \frac{1}{16}$

d)   $\frac{6}{11} - \frac{3}{7}$

e)   $2\frac{1}{3} \cdot 3\frac{2}{5}$

f)   $\frac{7}{10} \div \frac{3}{5}$

JM-133. The following graph represents a comparison of mileage to dollars spent on gas for nine people.

a) Of all the people graphed, which person drives the median number of miles each month?

b) Of all the people graphed, which person spends the median amount on gas each month?

c) What is the mode for the number of miles driven each month?

d) What is the mode for the amount of money spent on gasoline each month?

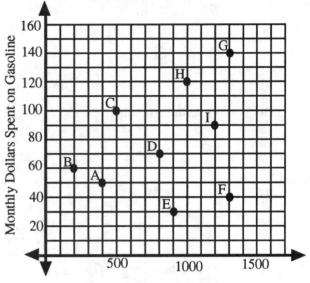

JM-134. At banquets, restaurants add a 15% service charge to the cost of the meal. The Little League awards banquet had a large turnout of 200 people. The cost per person for the meal was $6.95.

a) What was the cost for the meals?

b) What was the service charge?

c) What was the total bill?

d) What do you think the Little League should charge each person to attend the awards banquet? Explain your reasoning.

JM-135. Simplify the following expressions.

a) $-7 - (4(14 + 2 + (-10) + 5))$

b) $\dfrac{3 - 2 + 6 + 2}{2(14 - 2) \cdot 2}$

c) $\dfrac{56 - 4 \cdot \frac{1}{2} + 3.2}{8 + 2.4}$

d) $3.2 + 8 \cdot \dfrac{3}{5} - 5$

JM-136.   Simplify.

a)   $3\frac{4}{5} + 1\frac{9}{10}$                               b)   $1\frac{4}{9} - 4\frac{1}{3}$

c)   $7\frac{7}{8} \cdot 2\frac{7}{10}$                              d)   $6\frac{4}{9} \div 1\frac{3}{8}$


JM-137.   Write the given numbers and continue each pattern on your paper.

a)   $\frac{1}{8}, \frac{1}{4}, \frac{3}{8}$, _____, _____, _____, _____, _____

b)   $\frac{1}{6}, \frac{1}{3}$, _____, _____, $\frac{5}{6}$, _____

c)   _____, $\frac{2}{5}, \frac{0}{5}$, _____, $-\frac{4}{5}$, _____, _____

d)   0.25, _____, 0.75, _____, 1.25, _____, _____

e)   0.2, 0.05, _____, _____, _____, _____, -0.7

f)   7%, 15%, 31%, _____, _____, _____, _____


JM-138.   If the probability of an event happening is N, what is the probability of the event <u>not</u>
   happening?

(A)   N – 1         (B)   1 – N         (C)   1 + N         (D)   1 · N

JM-139. Becoming a professional basketball player is the dream of many students. Here are some numbers to consider. There are 150,000 high school seniors who play basketball every year. 3800 of them make it to a college team. Of those, 64 students make it to a professional team. (Source: NCAA.)

a) Slim is a high school senior on the basketball team in a large city. There are 1000 seniors in his league. Use a proportion to find how many of the 1000 students will make it onto a college team.

b) Use a proportion to find the number of those 1000 students who will make it onto a professional team.

c) What is the probability that a high school senior basketball player will make it to a professional team? Express your answer as a percent.

d) Refer to problem JM-35. Determine if the following statement is true or false: "It is about half as likely for a high school senior to become a professional basketball player as it is for him to become a professional football player."

JM-140. **What We Have Done in This Chapter**

Below is a list of the Tool Kit entries from this chapter.

- JM-7     Vocabulary Terms for Probability
- JM-13    Experimental and Theoretical Probabilities
- JM-17    Dependent and Independent Events
- JM-91    Population and Samples

When you have finished, write "My Tool Kit is up to date."

JM-141. **Course Summary** Your teacher will assign each team a chapter to summarize.

a) For your chapter, list the objectives from the front of the chapter. Restate them in your own words.

b) List the Tool Kit entries from the end of the chapter.

c) With your team select five problems from the chapter that you think best represent the objectives and Tool Kit.

d) Write out the solutions for the problems.

e) Prepare a poster to present to the rest of the class showing the chapter objectives (in your own words), the Tool Kit list, and the five problems with their solutions. Be ready to explain why you chose those particular problems.

JM-142. Your job is to create some new problems for the final exam. Your teacher will assign your team another chapter. Use the five problems selected for that chapter as a basis for writing the new problems. Sometimes you can do this by just changing some numbers. Sometimes you will need to change the whole problem. Two examples are given below.

Find the area.

Original:                                New:

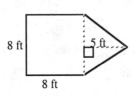

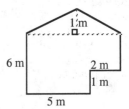

Solve the equation.

Original:  $5(x - 3) = -7x + 18$          New:  $-3(x - 5) = -2x + 10$

a) With your team, write one problem that is similar to but different from each of the five poster problems.

b) Solve each of the problems your team wrote.


JM-143. **A Letter of Advice**  Write a letter of advice to a student entering *Foundations for Algebra* for the first time. Include in this letter how they can be successful in this course. If you could start over, what would you do differently? What types of things helped you succeed in this class? What tools were important? What general advice would you give this student?

# *Appendix A*
## *Making the Order of Operations Formal:* MATHEMATICAL NAMES

## INTRODUCTION

So far in this book, we have tried to help you understand the ideas behind what you are doing. Now is the time to give the formal names to what you already understand, so that when someone asks you for a reason for your actions, you can give them a name for your reason—rather like being able to name a period in history (early Roman Empire) or a scientific effect (evaporation). Therefore, much of this Interlude will be telling rather than asking you to work on problems. Then, after we have told you the names that mathematicians give certain ideas, we will give you some examples and then more problems for practice.

## BACKGROUND

Mathematicians did not just sit down one day many years ago and make up the properties we will be talking about. Each of these properties comes from working with the whole numbers (0, 1, 2, 3, ...) and seeing the rules which always work for them. One such rule is $A \cdot B = B \cdot A$ for any two natural numbers A and B. This is not a surprise to you. You have known for a long time that, for example, $3 \cdot 4 = 4 \cdot 3$. What is different, however, is that many years ago, people studying algebra decided it was important to give this rule a name (the Commutative Property) and—this is the important part—to say that this rule works for <u>all</u> numbers. We use this property when we work with any kind of numbers: positive, negative, fractions, and even some kinds of numbers you may not know yet, like complex numbers. But once you have learned these rules and learned how to use them, you can be sure that they will always work. So the rule we gave earlier ($A \cdot B = B \cdot A$) is true even if A and B are these other kinds of numbers.

## THE PROPERTIES OF ARITHMETIC OPERATIONS AND THEIR FORMAL NAMES

**Additive Identity**  This is just the number zero (0). The name comes from the fact that when you add zero to any number, you get the same number you started with. That is, $x + 0 = x$ for any number x. This property is actually how the additive identity is defined: z is the additive identity if, for every number x, $z + x = x + z = x$. But you know it is the number zero.

**Additive Inverse**  An inverse operation in general is about undoing. Suppose you have the number 4 and want to add something to it to get zero (the additive identity). The number you would have to add would be -4. So we say that -4 is the additive inverse of 4. Similarly, the additive inverse of -3 is 3 since $(-3) + 3 = 0$. So, just like the previous definition, we say that for any number x, we get its additive inverse y if $x + y = y + x = 0$.

**Multiplicative Identity**  The number one (1). Just as adding the additive identity to a number does not change it, multiplying a number by the multiplicative identity does not change that number. So w is the multiplicative identity if, for every number x, $w \cdot x = x \cdot w = x$.

**Multiplicative Inverse**  Suppose you have the number 4 and want to multiply it by something to get 1 (the multiplicative identity). You would have to multiply by $\frac{1}{4}$. So we say $\frac{1}{4}$ is the multiplicative inverse of 4. Similarly, the multiplicative inverse of $\frac{1}{8}$ is 8 since $8 \cdot \frac{1}{8} = 1$. Formally, y is the multiplicative inverse of x if $x \cdot y = y \cdot x = 1$. An important fact to know is that zero does not have a multiplicative inverse, but it is the only number which does not.

**Distributive Property** You have worked with this property a lot so far, and it is enormously important in algebra where you will need it almost every day. It relates addition and multiplication and says that $x \cdot (y + z) = x \cdot y + x \cdot z$. Usually you would just write $x(y + z) = xy + xz$, but we put in the multiplication signs to emphasize the multiplicative aspects of this property.

**Commutative Property** We referred to the commutative property above. It simply says that the order in which you add or multiply does not matter. That is, for any two numbers $x$ and $y$, it is true that $x + y = y + x$ and $x \cdot y = y \cdot x$. Technically, there are two properties here: the commutative property of addition and the commutative property of multiplication. We will refer to both of them under the single name, "Commutative Property."

**Associative Property** This is one property that has probably never occurred to you ever to doubt. It says that if you have three numbers to add (or to multiply), if you add the first two and then add the sum to the third, you get the same answer as if you add the second and third and then add that sum to the first. Here it is in symbolic form remembering that we do operations inside of parentheses first, $(x + y) + z = x + (y + z)$ and $(x \cdot y) \cdot z = x \cdot (y \cdot z)$ or, if we write it without the multiplication symbol, $(xy)z = x(yz)$. So, for example, $(3 + 4) + 5 = 7 + 5 = 12$, which is also the answer of $3 + (4 + 5) = 3 + 9$. Again, technically, there are two properties here: the associative property of addition and the associative property of multiplication. We will refer to both of them under the single name, "Associative Property."

## EXAMPLES

Example 1.   Find $20 \cdot 12$. We know that $12 = 10 + 2$, so by the Distributive Property, we know that $20 \cdot 12 = 20 \cdot (10 + 2) = 20 \cdot 10 + 20 \cdot 2 = 200 + 40 = 240$.

Example 2.   Simplify $2x + 4 + 7x$. By the Commutative Property, we know that $4 + 7x = 7x + 4$. Now the problem becomes $2x + 7x + 4$. Using the usual order of operations, we solve this as $(2x + 7x) + 4$. Using the Distributive Property, $(2 + 7)x + 4 = 9x + 4$.

Example 3.   Show that $\frac{3}{4}$ and $\frac{24}{32}$ represent the same number. Using the Multiplicative Identity, $\frac{3}{4} \cdot 1 = \frac{3}{4}$. But when we write 1 as the Giant **1**, $\frac{8}{8}$, we see that $\frac{3}{4} \cdot \frac{8}{8} = \frac{24}{32}$. Thus, $\frac{3}{4} = \frac{24}{32}$.

## PROBLEMS

**MN-1.** Name the rule that allows us to do each of the following operations.

a) $4 + (5 + (-5)) = (4 + 5) + -5$

b) $5 \cdot 3 = 3 \cdot 5$

c) $3(x + 5) = 3x + 3 \cdot 5$

d) $14 + (-3) = -3 + 14$

e) $5 \cdot \frac{1}{5} = 1$

f) $\frac{2}{3} \cdot \frac{1}{6} = \frac{1}{6} \cdot \frac{2}{3}$

g) $x + 7z = 7z + x$

h) $13 + 0 = 13 + (-10 + 10)$

i) $7(x + yz) = 7x + 7yz$

j) $(z - w) \cdot 8 = 8 \cdot (z - w)$

k) $t + 0 = t$

**MN-2.** Name the operation that allows us to do $1 \cdot 7 = 7 \cdot 1$.

(A) Multiplicative Inverse

(B) Distributive Property

(C) Commutative Property

(D) Additive Identity

**MN-3.** Name the operation that allows us to do $1 \cdot 7 = 7$.

(A) Multiplicative Identity

(B) Distributive Property

(C) Commutative Property

(D) Additive Identity

**MN-4.** Name the operation that allows us to do $3 + (4 + 5) = 3 + (5 + 4)$.

(A) Multiplicative Identity

(B) Associative Property

(C) Distributive Property

(D) Commutative Property

**MN-5.** Name the operation that allows us to do $3 + (4 + 5) = (3 + 4) + 5$.

(A) Multiplicative Identity

(B) Associative Property

(C) Distributive Property

(D) Commutative Property

MN-6. Name the operation that allows us to do  -3 + 0 = -3.

(A) Additive Identity                    (B) Additive Inverse

(C) Distributive Property              (D) Associative Property


MN-7. Name the operation that allows us to do  -3 + 0 = -3 + (-6 + 6).

(A) Additive Identity                    (B) Additive Inverse

(C) Distributive Property              (D) Associative Property


## WHY A NEGATIVE TIMES A NEGATIVE IS A POSITIVE

Earlier in the course we gave an argument of why a negative integer times a negative integer is a positive integer which was primarily based on the idea that multiplying, say, $(-3) \cdot (-5)$ could be thought of as taking away 5 of the negative tiles and doing it 3 times. While most students come away from this demonstration knowing what the rule is and having a good idea why it works, the argument is more of a teaching device than a formal proof. Now, however, with the formal properties we introduced above, we can give a complete and formal demonstration of this fact.

The central idea in our proof uses the distributive property and the additive identity. We give two arguments which are actually exactly the same except that one is a purely formal proof which really uses algebra while the other one just uses a particular pair of numbers x and y. Reading over this proof will probably be difficult for most students, but if you think you might want to be a mathematician someday, it is never too early to get started. It will probably be easier if you start with the proof for Statement 1 that involves numbers. Then go to the more general one that uses variables.


### Statement 1   If  x  is a positive number and  y  is a negative number, then  xy  is negative.

We assume everyone knows three facts:
- If  x  and  z  are positive numbers, then their product is a positive number.
- The additive inverse of a positive number is negative and the additive inverse of a negative number is positive.
- If  x  is any number, then  $x \cdot 0 = 0$.

*Reasons that Statement 1 is true using a particular pair of numbers.*

Suppose  $x = 5$  and  $y = -3$. Then the additive inverse of  y  is 3 since $(-3) + 3 = 0$. Now see what happens when we multiply  $5 \cdot ((-3) + 3)$. We are going to treat  $5 \cdot (-3)$  as an unknown and get information about it.

By the Distributive Property, we know that  $5 \cdot ((-3) + 3) = 5 \cdot (-3) + 5 \cdot 3$. However, we also know that  $5 \cdot ((-3) + 3) = 5 \cdot 0 = 0$. (Recall we assumed that  $x \cdot 0 = 0$  for any number  x.) Therefore, the two products  $5 \cdot (-3)$  and  $5 \cdot 3$  are additive inverses since they add up to 0. But earlier we agreed that since 5 and 3 are positive, we know their product is positive. So their additive inverse—here $5 \cdot (-3)$—must be negative. So, at least for these two numbers with different signs, their product is negative.

*Reasons that Statement 1 is true using algebra.*

As stated, we assume that x is positive and y is negative. The additive inverse of y is (-y), which we know is positive. Now see what happens when we multiply $x \cdot (y + (-y))$. We are going to treat $x \cdot y$ as an unknown and get information about it.

By the Distributive Property, we know that $x \cdot (y + (-y)) = x \cdot y + x \cdot (-y)$. However, we also know that $x \cdot (y + (-y)) = x \cdot 0 = 0$. Therefore, the two products $x \cdot y$ and $x \cdot (-y)$ are additive inverses since they add up to 0. But earlier we agreed that since x and (-y) are positive, we know their product is positive. So their additive inverse—here $x \cdot y$—must be negative. Thus for any two numbers x and y, with x positive and y negative, their product is negative.

Now (at last) we are ready to show that a negative times a negative is a positive.

### Statement 2 If x and y are negative numbers, then xy is positive.

*Reasons that Statement 2 is true using a particular pair of numbers.*

Suppose x = -5 and y = -4. Then the additive inverse of y is 4 since (-4) + 4 = 0. Now see what happens when we multiply $(-5) \cdot ((-4) + 4)$.

By the Distributive Property, we know that $(-5) \cdot ((-4) + 4) = (-5) \cdot (-4) + (-5) \cdot 4$. However, we also know that $(-5) \cdot ((-4) + 4) = 5 \cdot 0 = 0$. Therefore, the two products $(-5) \cdot (-4)$ and $(-5) \cdot 4$ are additive inverses since they add up to 0. But since (-5) is negative and 4 is positive, by what we learned from Statement 1, we know their product is negative. So their additive inverse—here $(-5) \cdot (-4)$—must be positive. So, at least for these two numbers with negative signs, their product is positive.

*Reasons that Statement 2 is true using algebra.*

As stated, we assume that x and y are both negative. The additive inverse of y is (-y), which we know is positive. Now see what happens when we multiply $x \cdot (y + (-y))$.

Again, by the Distributive Property, we know that $x \cdot (y + (-y)) = x \cdot y + x \cdot (-y)$. However, we also know that $x \cdot (y + (-y)) = x \cdot 0 = 0$. Therefore, the two products $x \cdot y$ and $x \cdot (-y)$ are additive inverses since they add up to 0. But since x is negative and (-y) is positive, by what we learned from Statement 1, we know their product is negative. So their additive inverse—here $x \cdot y$—must be positive. Thus for any two negative numbers x and y, their product is positive.

### PROBLEM

MN-8.    In what we just did, we assumed that you knew that $x \cdot 0 = 0$ for any x. Actually, you can prove this statement, too, using the Distributive Property and the Additive Identity. As a hint, multiply the statement $1 + 0 = 1$ on both sides by x and see what happens.

# GLOSSARY

**absolute value:** ( | | ) The distance of a number from zero. It is always non-negative. (56)

**acute angle:** An angle with a measure of less than 90°. (101)

**acute triangle:** A triangle with all three angle measures less than 90°. (101)

**addition:** ( + ) An operation that tells how many things there are when two sets are combined. The result is the number of objects in the two sets together, called a sum. In arithmetic, the word "object" usually means "number." (38, 224)

**adjacent angles:** Angles which share a common side and vertex but no common interior points. (281)

**algebra:** A branch of mathematics that uses variables to generalize the rules of numbers and numerical operations.

**algebraic expression:** Variables and constants, possibly joined by operations. Examples: 3x or 2x + 4 (78)

**algorithm:** A fixed rule for carrying out a mathematical procedure. Example: To find the average of a set of values, find their sum and divide by the number of values.

**altitude of a triangle (height):** The perpendicular distance from a vertex to the opposite side (or its extension) of a triangle.

**angle:** A geometric figure made up of two rays or line segments that have the same endpoint. (101)

**arc:** The portion of a circle between two points on a circle.

**area:** The measure in square units of the interior region of a plane figure or the surface of a three dimensional figure. (103)

**area of triangle:** To find the area of a triangle, multiply the length of the base by the height and divide by two. $A = \frac{1}{2} bh$ (117)

**area of a circle:** $A = \pi r^2$, where r is the length of the radius of the circle. See area. (331)

**associative property for addition:** Changing the grouping of the numbers does not change the result in addition. Example: $(5 + 3) + 7 = 5 + (3 + 7)$ (308)

**associative property for multiplication:** Changing the grouping of the numbers does not change the result in multiplication. Example: $(5 \cdot 3) \cdot 2 = 5 \cdot (3 \cdot 2)$ (308)

**average (mean):** The sum of given numbers divided by the number of numbers used in computing the sum. Example: The average of 1, 4, and 10 is $(1 + 4 + 10) \div 3 = 5$. (11)

**axis (pl. axes):** A number line which can be used to indicate a position of a point, based on its coordinates. (43)

**base of an exponent:** The number used as the factor in an exponential expression. Example: $5^2 = 5 \cdot 5$. 5 is the base.

**base:** For a triangle, the base may be any side, although usually it is the bottom one. For a trapezoid, the two parallel sides are the bases. For a cylinder or prism, either one of the two congruent parallel faces may be the base while for a pyramid or cone, the base is the (flat) face which does not contain the vertex (where all the sides come together). (101, 108, 117)

**biased question:** A question is biased if it makes assumptions about the person being questioned or if it makes one answer seem better than another. (378)

**bimodal:** A set of numbers that has two modes.

**causality:** When one event causes another to occur. (396)

**certainty:** When an event will definitely happen. The probability of a certain event is 1. (363)

**center:** (or center point) The point equidistant from all points on a circle. (323)

**central angle:** An angle whose vertex is the center of a circle.

**chord:** A line segment that connects two points on a circle.

**circle:** The set of all points in two dimensions that are the same distance r from a fixed point P. The fixed point P is called the center of the circle and the distance r is called the radius. (101, 323)

**circumference:** The distance around the outside of a circle. You can calculate circumference by multiplying $\pi$ by the length of the diameter. $C = \pi d = 2\pi r$. (327)

**closed option:** A question with a limited number of possible answers. (383)

**coefficient (numerical):** The numeral part of a term, such as 6 in 6x.

**combining like terms:** When working with an expression, terms with the same variables (with the same exponents) can be combined into one quantity. Numbers are combined by addition and subtraction. Example: $3x^2 + 2y + 6 + 4y - 2x^2 = x^2 + 6y + 6$. (298)

**common:** Shared.

**common factor:** A common term factor: (1) in arithmetic, the integers multiplied are called factors; (2) in algebra, a monomial or polynomial that is a factor of a polynomial. For example: $10x + 15 = 5 \cdot 2x + 5 \cdot 3 = 5(2x + 3)$. Five is the common factor.

**common multiple:** A number that is a multiple of the two or more numbers. Example: 24 and 48 are common multiples of 3 and 8. (186)

**commutative property:** The property of an operation such that changing the order of the numbers does not change the result of the operation. Examples: $3 \cdot 4 = 4 \cdot 3$ or $7 + 8 = 8 + 7$ (308)

**complementary angles:** Two angles whose sum is 90°. (281)

**complementary probabilities:** Two probabilities are complementary if their sum is one.

**complex fraction:** A fraction with a fraction in the numerator and/or the denominator. (254)

**composite figure:** A shape made of several simpler figures. (121)

**composite number:** A number with more than two factors.

**compound events:** A combination of simple events.

**congruent:** Figures which have the same size and shape. (106)

**conjecture:** An educated guess, based on data, patterns, and data. Scientists use the term hypothesis. (96)

**consecutive:** In order. Example: 8, 9,10 are consecutive numbers. (315)

**constant:** A numerical term which does not change.

**coordinate grid (system):** A two dimensional system formed by two perpendicular number lines that intersect at their zero points. The location of a point is given by first stating the horizontal location (x) and then the vertical location (y), written as an ordered pair, (x, y). (43)

**correlation:** A measure of interdependence of two sets of data. (395)

**cross multiplication:** A way to find a missing numerator or denominator in equivalent fractions by multiplying diagonally across the equal sign to get an equivalent equation without fractions. Example: In $\frac{a}{b} = \frac{c}{d}$, after cross multiplication the equation would be ad = bc. (183)

**cube:** A rectangular prism with 6 congruent faces, all squares.

**cubic unit:** A cube each of whose edges measures 1 unit in length. Volume is measured in cubic units..

**cylinder:** Commonly, a three dimensional object with two circular, congruent, and parallel bases. (344)

**decimal point:** The dot separating the ones and tenths places in a decimal number.

**denominator:** The lower part of a fraction which tells into how many equal parts the whole is divided. (156)

**dependent events:** Two events are dependent if the outcome of the first event affects the outcome of the second event. (366)

**diagonal:** A segment that joins two vertices of a polygon and is not one of the sides. (101)

**diameter:** A line segment that has its endpoints on the circle and passes through the center. The longest chord in a circle. (323)

**difference:** The answer to a subtraction problem. (73)

**digit:** One of the ten numerals: 0, 1, 2, 3, 4, 5, 6, 7, 8, 9.

**distributive property:** For any a, b, and c, a (b + c) = ab + ac. Example: 10(7 + 2) = 10·7 + 10·2 (303)

**dividend:** A quantity to be divided. See: divisor.

**divisible:** A number is divisible by another if their remainder is zero.

**division:** The inverse operation to multiplication  The operation which creates equal groups. (29, 183, 248, 263)

**divisor:** The quantity by which another quantity is to be divided.  dividend ÷ divisor = quotient

**edge:** The line segment where two faces of a solid figure meet.

**endpoint:** Either of the two points which mark the ends of a line segment.

**equal:** Having the same value. (4)

**equal ratios:** Two equivalent fractions; a proportion. (166)

**equation:** A mathematical sentence relating two mathematical expressions with an equal sign (=). (4)

**equilateral triangle:** A triangle with all three sides the same length. (101)

**equivalent:** Naming the same amount with a different name. (149)

**evaluate (an expression):** To evaluate an expression, substitute the value(s) given for the variable(s) and perform the operations according to the order of operations. (298)

**even number:** A whole number divisible by two with no remainder.

**event:** One or more results of an experiment. (363)

**experimental probability:** Probability based upon the results of an experiment.
$$P(\text{event}) = \frac{\text{\# of times an event occurs}}{\text{\# of times the experiment took place}} \quad (365)$$

**exponent:** In the expression $2^5$, 5 is called the exponent. The exponent indicates how many times to use the base as a multiplier.

**expression:** See algebraic expression. (78)

**face:** A polygonal region of a three-dimensional figure. (337)

**factor:** When two or more numbers are multiplied, each of the numbers multiplied is a factor of the product.

**factored form:** Use the distributive property to change from a sum to a product. Example: 10x + 15 = 5(2x + 3)

**formula:** An equation that shows a mathematical relationship.

**fraction:** A number expressed in the form $\frac{a}{b}$ where a and b are whole numbers, b ≠ zero. (9)

**frequency:** The number of times something occurs in an interval or in a data set.

**graph:** A visual display of information in an organized manner. (43)

**greatest common factor (GCF):** The largest number which will divide evenly into two or more numbers. Example: 6 is the greatest common factor of 12 and 18.

**guess and check table:** A problem solving strategy in which you begin by making a guess and then check whether or not your answer is correct. In the process of checking, you gain information about how close your guess might be and make adjustments to your guess. Being organized is crucial to the success of this method, as well as writing a usable table. Guess and check leads to writing equations to represent word problems. (70)

**height (altitude):** The perpendicular distance between 2 bases, or a vertex and a base. See altitude. (105, 108, 117)

**hexagon:** A polygon with six sides. (101)

**horizontal:** Parallel to the horizon. The x-axis in a coordinate grid. (43)

**identity property of addition:** Zero is the identity for addition: It does not change the value of a number when added to the number. (405)

**identity property of multiplication:** One is the identity element for multiplication. Multiplying by one does not change the value of a number. (159)

**impossibility:** An event with a probability of zero. (363)

**independent events:** Two events are independent if the outcome of the first event does not depend on the outcome of the second event. (366)

**inequality:** A mathematical sentence which compares two quantities, showing they are not the same. The symbols used may be: < (less than), > (greater than), to), or ≠ (not equal to). (157)

**integers:** The set of numbers { . . ., -3, -2, -1, 0, 1, 2, 3,... } (27)

**interval:** A set of numbers between two given numbers.

**irrational numbers:** Numbers that can not be written as the ratio of two integers.

**inverse operations:** An operation that undoes another operation. Example: multiplication is the inverse operation for division. (56)

**isosceles triangle:** A triangle with at least two sides equal in length. (101)

**least common multiple (LCM):** The smallest common multiple of set of two or more numbers. Example: the least common multiple of 4 and 6 is 12. (187)

**like terms:** Terms that have the same variable part and corresponding exponent. 5 and 19 are like terms, 3xy and 5xy are like terms, $6x^2$ and $-3x^2$ are like terms. (298)

**line:** An infinite set of points forming a straight path extending in two directions.

**line segment:** A part of a line with endpoints. (101)

**linear equation:** An equation whose graph is a line, generated by an equation with a linear expression in it.

**linear expression:** An expression in the form of ax + b, where a and b are numbers.

**lowest common denominator (LCD):** The smallest common multiple of the denominators of two or more fractions. Example: The LCD of $\frac{5}{12}$ and $\frac{3}{8}$ is 24. (223)

**mean:** A measure of central tendency often referred to as the average. See average. (11)

**measure of central tendency:** Mean, median, and mode are all measures of central tendency, reflecting specific statistical information about a set of data. (20)

**median:** The middle number of a set of ordered data. If there is no distinct middle, the average of the two middle numbers is the median. (15)

**mode:** The number or numbers that show up the most in a set of data. There can be more than one mode. (11)

**midpoint:** The point on a line segment that divides the line segment into two congruent line segments.

**mixed number (fraction):** A number with an integer component and a fraction component. Example: $2\frac{3}{4}$ (147)

**multiple:** The product of a whole number and any other (non-zero) whole number. Example: 15 is a multiple of five.

**multiplication:** An operation which reflects repeated addition. Example: $3 \cdot 4 = 4 + 4 + 4$. (49, 236, 261)

**natural numbers:** The counting numbers beginning with 1. Example: 1, 2, 3...

**negative numbers:** Numbers which are less than zero, designated with a − sign. (27)

**negative correlation:** A relationship between two sets of variables in which one generally increases as the other decreases. (396)

**net:** A two dimensional one-piece plan which can be folded into a three dimensional shape. (347)

**number line:** A diagram representing all real numbers as points on a line. (27)

**numeral:** An expression (which is not a variable) that names a particular number.

**numerator:** The number above the bar in a fraction which tells the number of parts in relationship to the number of parts in the whole.

**numerical order:** To write numbers from smallest to largest. (15)

**obtuse angle:** An angle greater than 90° and less than 180˚. (101)

**octagon:**  A polygon with eight sides.  (101)

**odd number:**  A whole number which can not be evenly divided by 2.

**open option:**  A question which allows free response.  (383)

**operation:**  In mathematics, addition, subtraction, multiplication, division, raising to a power and taking a root are operations.  (72)

**order of operations:**  Rules which define in what sequence operations will be completed when an expression is presented for evaluation. Expressions inside parentheses are evaluated first, then multiplication or division (left to right) followed by addition and subtraction (left to right).  (81)

**origin:**  The point assigned to zero on the number line or the point where the x- and y-axes intersect in a coordinate system.  (43)

**ordered pair:**  A pair of numbers (a, b) used to indicate a position on a coordinate plane.  The first number indicates the horizontal coordinate; the second number indicates the vertical coordinate. Syn: coordinate.  (43)

**outcome:**  Possible results in an experiment or consequence of an action.  (363)

**parallel:**  ( $\parallel$ ) Two lines which never intersect and are the same distance apart are said to be parallel. (101)

**parallelogram:**  A quadrilateral with opposite sides parallel.  (101)

**pentagon:**  A polygon with five sides.  (101)

**percent:** ( % )  A ratio that compares a number to 100.  (75, 199)

**perfect square:**  The product of an integer times itself gives a perfect square.  Example:  1, 4, and 9 are perfect squares because $1 = 1 \cdot 1$;  $4 = 2 \cdot 2$;  $9 = 3 \cdot 3$;  $16 = 4 \cdot 4$...

**perimeter:**  The distance around a figure on a flat surface.  (62)

**perpendicular:**  ( $\perp$ ) Lines, segments, or rays that intersect to form right angles.  (101)

**pi ($\pi$):**  The ratio of a circle's circumference to its diameter.  An irrational number, it is common to use the approximation of 3.14 or $\frac{22}{7}$ if you are not using a scientific calculator with a $\pi$ key.  (326)

**place value:**  The value of a position of a digit in a number.

**plane:**  A flat surface that extends infinitely in all directions.  It has no thickness.

**point:**  An exact location in space.  In two dimensions, an ordered pair specifies a point in a coordinate plane.  (43)

**poll:**  (verb) To ask questions in a survey or election, (noun) a survey.  (373)

**polygon:**  A two dimensional closed figure with straight line segments connected end to end. The segments may not cross.  Examples:  triangle or quadrilateral.  (101)

**polyhedron:** A three dimensional figure in which all surfaces are polygons.

**population:** A collection of objects or group of people about whom information is gathered. (388)

**power(exponent):** See exponent.

**positive correlation:** A relationship between two sets of variables in which one generally increases as the other increases. (395)

**positive numbers:** Numbers that a greater than zero.

**prime:** A number with exactly two factors. Examples: 2, 3, 5, 7...

**prime factorization:** The expression of a number as the product of prime factors.

**prism:** A 3 dimensional figure composed of polygonal faces and two parallel, congruent faces called bases, no holes are permitted in the solid. The remaining faces are parallelograms (or other special quadrilaterals). A prism is named for the shape of its base. (337)

**probability:** The chance of an event happening. When the outcomes are equally likely, it equals the number of event outcomes divided by the total number of outcomes. Example: when rolling a number cube, the probability that you will roll a $3 = \dfrac{1 \text{ way}}{6 \text{ possible outcomes}} = \dfrac{1}{6}$. (363)

**product ( $\cdot$ ):** Result of multiplying. Example: 72 is the product of $8 \cdot 9$. (83)

**proportion:** Two equivalent ratios. Example: $\dfrac{1}{3} = \dfrac{3}{9}$ (166)

**quadrants:** The four sections of a coordinate grid.

**quadrilateral:** A polygon with four sides. (101)

**quotient:** The result of a division problem.

**radius:** (plural: **radii**) The distance from the center to a point on the circle. (323)

**random sample:** A sample in which each item in the population or sample space has an equal chance of being selected. (388)

**range:** In statistics, the difference between the least and greatest pieces of data. (11)

**rate:** A ratio comparing two quantities, often a comparison of time. Example: miles per hour.

**ratio:** A comparison of two numbers which can indicate division. It can be written three ways: 2 boys to 5 girls, 2 boys : 5 girls, or $\dfrac{2 \text{ boys}}{5 \text{ girls}}$. (145)

**rational number:** A number that can be written in the form $\dfrac{a}{b}$ with a and b integers and $b \neq$ zero.

**ray:** A portion of a line that has one endpoint and extends forever in one direction. (101)

**real numbers:** The set of rational and irrational numbers. (All the numbers on the number line.)

**reciprocals:** Two numbers which have a product of 1. Example: 2 and $\frac{1}{2}$ are reciprocals of each other. (250)

**rectangle:** A quadrilateral with four right angles. Its two pairs of opposite sides are parallel and congruent. (101)

**reduce:** To put a fraction into simplest form. (240)

**regular polygon:** A polygon in which all sides are congruent and all angles have the same measure. (101)

**representative sample:** A subset (group) of a given population with the same characteristics as the population. (388)

**rhombus:** A quadrilateral with four congruent sides. (101)

**right angle:** An angle with a measure of 90°. (101)

**right triangle:** A triangle with one right angle in it. (101)

**root:** A number that can be used as a factor a given number of times. Example: The square root of 16 is 4 because $4 \cdot 4 = 16$. $\sqrt{16} = 4$

**sample:** A subgroup selected from a larger group. (388)

**sample space:** The set of all possible outcomes from which a sample is taken, often the same as the population. (363)

**scale (scaling):** An arrangement of numbers in uniform intervals. (25)

**scalene triangle:** A triangle with no two sides of equal length. (101)

**scatter plot:** Two related sets of data graphed as points; often in a coordinate plane. *See positive and negative correlation.* (395)

**scientific notation:** A method of writing very large or very small numbers as a product of a power of ten and a number greater than or equal to one and less than 10. Example: $124{,}500 = 1.245 \cdot 10^5$

**sector:** A part of the interior of a circle bounded by two radii and the arc between their endpoints. (345)

**semi-circle:** Half of a circle. (343)

**set:** A collection of items. (248)

**similar figures:** Figures which are similar have the same shape but not necessarily the same size; the lengths of the corresponding sides are proportional to one another; the corresponding angles are congruent. (205)

**simplest form of a fraction:** A fraction whose numerator and denominator have no common factor greater than one. (240)

**simplify:** To combine like terms; to express the quantity using as few symbols as possible; to put a fraction in lowest terms. (240, 298)

**slope:** A way to specify the steepness of a line defined as the ratio of the vertical distance divided by the horizontal distance between any two points on the line.

**solution:** Any value for a variable that makes an equation true. (20)

**square:** A quadrilateral with four congruent sides and four right angles. (101)

**square number:** Any number which is the product of two identical whole numbers. (example: $1 \cdot 1 = 1,\ 2 \cdot 2 = 4,\ 3 \cdot 3 = 9$ ...)

**square root:** See root.

**square measure:** The units used to describe the measure of an area in the form of 1 x 1 unit squares. (103)

**stem and leaf plot:** A frequency distribution made by arranging the data. (17)

**straight angle:** A 180° angle. (274)

**subproblems:** A problem solving strategy which breaks a problem into smaller parts which must be solved in order to solve the original, complex problem. (121)

**substitution:** Replacing one symbol by another (a number, a variable, or other algebraic expression) without changing the value of the expression. (55)

**subtraction ( - ):** An operation that gives the difference between two numbers. (73, 224)

**sum:** An answer to a addition problem. (38)

**supplementary angles:** Two angles whose measurements give a sum of 180°. (281)

**surface area:** The total area of all faces and bases of a polyhedron, cylinder, cone, or pyramids. (348)

**survey:** (verb) To ask questions in a survey or election, (noun) a survey. *Syn: poll* (383)

**term:** Each part of the expression separated by addition or subtraction signs is a term. (81, 298)

**theoretical probability:** A probability calculated using the formula.
$$P = \frac{\text{\# of favorable outcomes}}{\text{\# of equally likely possible outcomes}} \quad (365)$$

**tick mark:** An indicator that a number line has been divided into intervals of equal length.

**trimodel:** A set of data that has three modes.

**trapezoid:** A quadrilateral with exactly one pair of parallel sides. (101)

**triangle:** A polygon with three sides. (101)

**unit fraction:** A fraction with a numerator of one.

**unit price:** The cost of one item or one measure of an item. Example: cost for one pound or one gallon. (201)

**unit rate:** A rate with a denominator of one. (202)

**units digit:** The numeral in the ones place.

**variable:** A symbol or letter that stands for a number. (20)

**vertex:** The point at which two rays, line segments, or lines meet. (101)

**vertical:** At right angles to the horizon. In a coordinate grid, the y axis runs vertically. (43)

**vertical angles:** The angles opposite each other when two lines intersect. (101)

**volume:** The number of cubic units inside a three dimensional object. (336)

**x-axis:** The horizontal number line on a coordinate grid. (43)

**x-intercepts:** The point(s) where a graph intersects the x-axis. The x-intercept always has coordinates (x, 0).

**y-axis:** The vertical number line on a coordinate grid. (43)

**y-intercepts:** The point(s) where a graph intersects the y-axis. The y-intercept always has coordinates (0, y).

# INDEX

## Chapter Prefixes

Many of the page numbers listed here contain the definitions or examples of the topic listed.  It may be necessary, however, to read text on preceding pages or the pages following to understand the topic fully.  Also, on some page numbers listed here you will find "good examples" of the topic, but they may not offer any explanation.  It is very important, therefore, for you to be sure you correct and complete your homework and keep it organized.  Your record of the problems related to these topics may be your best index to understanding the mathematics of this course.

# THIS BOOK IS THE PROPERTY OF:

Book No._____

| ISSUED TO | Year Used | CONDITION | |
|-----------|-----------|-----------|----------|
| | | ISSUED | RETURNED |
| | | | |
| | | | |
| | | | |
| | | | |
| | | | |
| | | | |
| | | | |
| | | | |
| | | | |

PUPILS to whom this textbook is issued must not write on any page or mark any part of it in any way, unless otherwise instructed by the teacher.